To my parents,
who didn't tell me not to.

First published in Great Britain in November 2022 by Indie Novella Ltd.

INDIE NOVELLA www.indienovella.co.uk

A CIP catalogue record for this title is available from the British Library.

ISBN 978 1 7399599 3 7

Printed and bound in the UK by Swallowtail Print, Drayton, Norwich
First printing November 2022
Second printing December 2022

Indie Novella is committed to a sustainable future for our readers and the world in which we live. All paper used is a natural, renewable and sustainable product.

Supported using public funding by
ARTS COUNCIL
ENGLAND

INTRODUCTION

I first encountered *The Worst Journey in the World* when BBC Radio 4 aired a partial dramatisation of it in the autumn of 2008. The story was so amazing, and the characters so wonderful, that I resisted seeking out the original book – I didn't want to find out that the truth was less amazing or wonderful than the version I'd fallen in love with. Hunger eventually drove me to it, though, and I discovered that not only was the radio drama remarkably truthful, but there was so much more to the story and characters. I had to learn more. I had to share it with people. And so the road to a graphic novel began.

I read everything I could get my hands on, and soon came to realise that the true story was better than anything a dramatist could concoct, but also that there was a lot of shoddy research out there. It became my mission to tell the story properly – to include the science, the personalities, and what happened *outside* of the famous "race" to the South Pole, because they all affected the course of events. And I was determined to stick to the truth as closely as possible, to show where every detail came from, and to flag any time narrative expediency demanded a deviation from the historical record. It would be a factually accurate retelling; I had only to acquire all the facts.

Eleven years later …

Falling down the research rabbit hole has been an incredible journey of its own, and its fruits are woven into every line on these pages (and my life, but that's another story). Inevitably, I have ended up with more information than will fit in a comic. This is where the annotations come in. Are you confused by something you've read? Curious to know more? You can probably find what you're looking for in the notes at the back of the book, and some surprises besides. Each comic page is represented there in miniature graphic form, with numbers on it that correspond to a note with further information. The annotations are completely optional – I hope you can read the comic for fun, and not feel it's homework – but they are there for you if you want a little extra. People seem to like them. Maybe you will, too. Here's how they work:

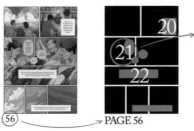

1. Find the page number
2. Find that page's icon in the annotations
3. Find the note you're curious about
4. Facts!

20. WJ 21, ed.

21. Cobbled together f

22. WJ 22, ed.

These pages are true not exactly false in the p impression of time and, if waves.

It was a race to get c and sunset at 6. Because

My ambition is to bring you an epic story from the pages of history, in a fun and engaging way. Girding it with cast-iron research is a matter of honour, both my own and on behalf of the people in the story. I hope you will enjoy it. If I take you away to another time and place for a while, and bring dead men briefly back to life, my job is done. If I introduce you to a subject which excites you and inspires further learning, I will be very pleased indeed. *The Worst Journey in the World* reconfigured my relationship with myself and the world: the story and the people were what I never knew I needed until they walked into my life, and I'm grateful for them every day. If my work can inspire even a few readers in the way I was inspired, then everything will have been worthwhile. But it's enough just to be able to share them with you.

S. AIRRIESS
Cambridge, 2022

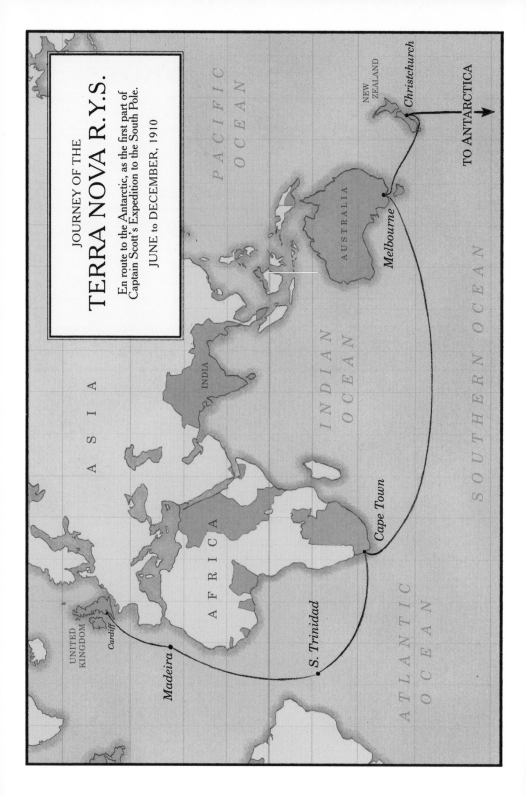

JOURNEY OF THE
TERRA NOVA R. Y. S.

En route to the Antarctic, as the first part of
Captain Scott's Expedition to the South Pole.

JUNE to DECEMBER, 1910

PACIFIC OCEAN

NEW ZEALAND

Christchurch

TO ANTARCTICA

AUSTRALIA

Melbourne

ASIA

INDIA

INDIAN OCEAN

AFRICA

Cape Town

SOUTHERN OCEAN

UNITED KINGDOM

Cardiff

Madeira

S. Trinidad

ATLANTIC OCEAN

PRINCIPAL PERSONAGES

Capt. ROBERT F. SCOTT
NICKNAME: "The Owner"

Commanding Officer,
Leader of the Expedition

Lt. EDWARD EVANS
NICKNAME: "Teddy"

Second-in-Command,
Skipper of the Terra Nova

Dr. EDWARD A. WILSON
NICKNAME: "Bill"

Head of Scientific Staff,
Vertebrate Zoologist, Artist

Lt. VICTOR CAMPBELL
NICKNAME: "Wicked Mate"

First Mate of the Terra Nova,
Leader of the Eastern Party

Lt. HARRY PENNELL
NICKNAME: "Penelope"

Navigator of the Terra Nova

Lt. HENRY R. BOWERS
NICKNAME: "Birdie"

Stores Officer

Dr. EDWARD ATKINSON
NICKNAME: "Atch"

Chief Medical Officer,
Biologist, Helminthologist

GEORGE C. SIMPSON
NICKNAME: "Sunny Jim"

Meteorologist

CHARLES S. WRIGHT
NICKNAME: "Silas"

Physicist, Chemist, Glaciologist

EDWARD W. NELSON
NICKNAME: "Marie"

Marine Biologist

Capt. LAWRENCE OATES
NICKNAME: "Titus"

Horse Expert,
"Adaptable Helper"

APSLEY CHERRY-GARRARD
NICKNAME: "Cherry"

Assistant Zoologist,
"Adaptable Helper"

P.O. EDGAR EVANS
NICKNAME: "Taff"

Petty Officer

P.O. THOMAS CREAN
NICKNAME: "Crean"

Petty Officer

The WORST JOURNEY *in the* WORLD

The Graphic Novel

Being a graphic narrative adaptation of
Apsley Cherry-Garrard's
classic account of

THE BRITISH ANTARCTIC EXPEDITION,
1910-13

Devised and drawn by
Sarah Airriess

Volume 1

MAKING OUR EASTING DOWN

Cardiff – Madeira – South Trinidad – Cape Town –
Melbourne – Christchurch – Dunedin – Antarctica

And is it that the haze of grief
      Makes former gladness loom so great?
      The lowness of the present state,
That sets the past in this relief?

Or that the past will always win
      A glory from its being far;
      And orb into the perfect star
We saw not, when we moved therein?

In Memoriam, XXIV

Polar exploration is at once the cleanest
and most isolated way of having a bad time
which has been devised.

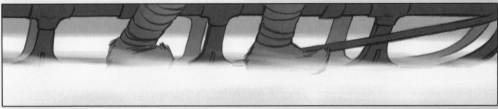

"Is it worth it?"   What is worth what?
Is life worth risking for a feat, or losing for your country?

To face a thing because it was a feat, and only a feat,
was not very attractive to Scott.

It had to contain an additional object—knowledge.

2

We pursued knowledge – most of us were not ambitious for personal gain: we simply wanted to know. We had the gift, the invaluable gift, of curiosity.

The greatest interest of all is what we human beings, all of us, will do voluntarily for an idea. What will we not do?

We kill and are killed; we persecute and torture; we suffer and die.

We overcome our
weaker natures.

Some
overcome
the world.

Though we achieved a first-rate tragedy,
    tragedy was not our business.

I am afraid it was all inevitable ...

LAMER PARK
HERTFORDSHIRE
1919

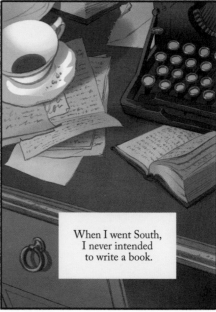

When I went South,
I never intended
to write a book.

When asked to, I discovered that I had intended to write one ever since I realized what had happened.

The mutual conquest of difficulties is the cement of friendship. We had plenty of difficulties; we sometimes failed, we sometimes won; we always faced them – we had to.

In a way, this book is a sequel to the friendship which there was between Wilson, Bowers, and myself, which, having stood the strain of the Winter Journey, could never have been broken.

But this was not my main object in writing this book.

When I undertook it, what I wanted to do above all things was to show what work was done, who did it, to whom the credit was due, and who pulled us through that last and most ghastly year, when God only knew what was best to be done.

Generally as a
mere follower,
without much
responsibility,
and often scared
out of my wits,
I was in the
thick of it all,
and I know.

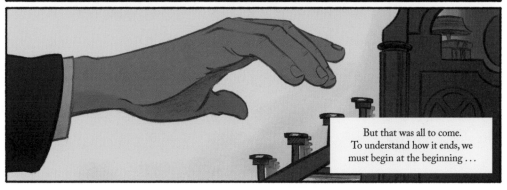

But that was all to come.
To understand how it ends, we
must begin at the beginning . . .

9

CARDIFF
JUNE 14th, 1910

10

Welcome aboard, Mr. Cherry-Garrard!

Very pleased to be here, Lieutenant Evans.

And we are very pleased to have you.

BOWERS! Come and show Mr. Cherry-Garrard to his cabin.

Taxidermy gear to the lazarette, please.

Welcome! Welcome!

You're in the wardroom, with the other scientists.

'Scuse us –

Campbell, who let Farmer Hayseed on board?

That's Captain Oates.

That's "No Surrender Oates"?!

" WE CAME HERE TO FIGHT, NOT TO SURRENDER ! ! "

He paid £1,000 for the privilege of being here, just like you, little millionaire.

13

Oh, well, I hope to be of some practical help, too . . .

Up this way is the galley –

Aha, Gran!

Ja?

!

PAF!

'S alright!

I say, what a splendid fellow!

Make way for Dr. Wilson!

Shake a long leg, Director, you're late!

Bill!

Good afternoon, Cherry! How splendid to see you here.

Ready for the big show?

I couldn't wait a moment longer.

Take good care of him, Cherry.

See you tonight.

Now, where have they put the taxidermy gear?

It's in the lazarette.

Oh, well done!

Before we could get away, we were fêted by the great and the good of the city of Cardiff, whose donations, both financial and material, had made the Expedition possible.

17

Scott used to say that the worst part of an expedition was over when the preparation was finished. No doubt it was with a sigh of relief that he saw the Terra Nova weigh anchor.

You ought to have a leek strung up there with the Welsh flag!

We've already got a leak in the fore peak!

But our leader would not be travelling with us all the way to New Zealand. There were funds yet to raise and contracts to negotiate, so he would join us by steamer later.

See you in Cape Town.

Scott was keen that, so far as was possible, the personnel of the expedition must go out with the Terra Nova, and crew her all the way to New Zealand, from whence we would embark for Antarctica.

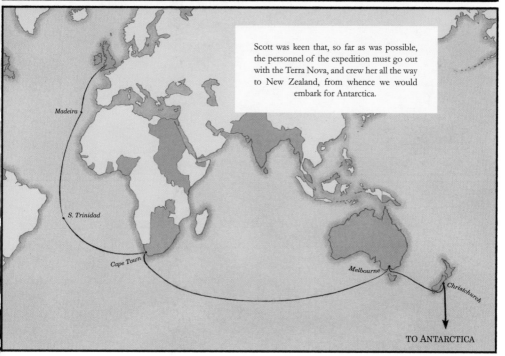

Possibly he gave instructions that they were to be worked hard, and no doubt it was a good opportunity of testing our mettle. We had been chosen out of 8,000 volunteers – officers, scientists, crew, and all.

The executive officers were drawn from the Navy, as were the crew.

Two of our doctors were naval surgeons with a side line in biology.

G. M. LEVICK

E. L. ATKINSON

The other – Wilson – was also chief of the scientific staff, vertebral zoologist, artist, and unfailing friend-in-need of all on board.

E. A. WILSON

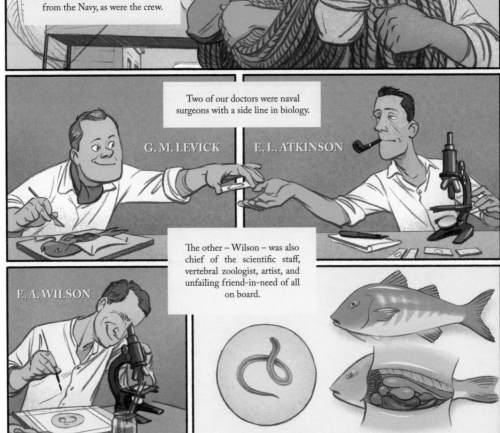

Nelson and Lillie were our marine biologists.

DENNIS LILLIE

EDWARD NELSON

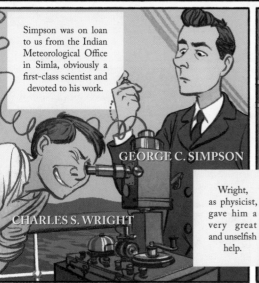

Simpson was on loan to us from the Indian Meteorological Office in Simla, obviously a first-class scientist and devoted to his work.

GEORGE C. SIMPSON

CHARLES S. WRIGHT

Wright, as physicist, gave him a very great and unselfish help.

TRYGGVE GRAN

Wright and I shared our cabin with Tryggve Gran, a Norwegian who Scott had recruited to teach us how to ski.

Two of the scientific staff were called "adaptable helpers," namely Oates and myself.

APSLEY CHERRY-GARRARD

LAWRENCE OATES

Oates would be in charge of the horses once we picked them up in New Zealand.

I was Wilson's aide and assistant zoologist.

The specialists were as eager to share their enthusiasm as the rest of us were eager to learn.

Bowers was proving himself the best seaman on board, with an exact knowledge of the whereabouts and contents of every case, box and bale, and with a supreme contempt for heat or cold.

Lt. HENRY R. BOWERS

PEACHES

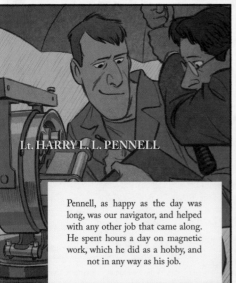

Lt. HARRY L. L. PENNELL

Pennell, as happy as the day was long, was our navigator, and helped with any other job that came along. He spent hours a day on magnetic work, which he did as a hobby, and not in any way as his job.

Every one whose work allowed turned immediately to any job which was wanted, and there was never any failure to respond fully.

We were to a great extent strangers to one another when we left England, but when men live close as we did they settle down or quarrel before very long.

The first days out were spent in such hard and crowded work that we shook down very quickly.

All hands to the pumps!

We were roused before six and turned on to the pumps.

The bilges needed to be pumped dry every watch, six times a day.

In South Australia I was born –

HEAVE AWAY, HAUL AWAY

South Australia, round Cape Horn –

We're bound for South Australia!

I didn't expect sailing would be mostly pumping.

A wooden ship always leaks a little.

This is a *little*?!

Well . . . she sails like a witch, anyway.

The ship was generally dry after over an hour's pumping.

The first thing to do was get a bath.

Lt. VICTOR CAMPBELL

Efforts in this direction would have been amusing had it not been for the caustic eye of Campbell, in whose hands the routine and discipline of the ship was most efficiently maintained.

I was very frightened of Campbell.

27

MADEIRA
JUNE 23rd, 1910

In Madeira, as everywhere, we were given freely of such things as we required, and each enjoyed the island as suited his fancy.

So hungry, I die in one minute.

Where is the cheese, half a minute gone.

THAT'S NEARLY OUR FOUR HOURS, I SHOULD THINK.

This is the sea-water soap, isn't it?

In name only.

Oh, look!

Nelson!

Come and see the dolphins!

Sigh...

33

All these numbers are making my head swim.

It sounds complicated, but the principle is actually quite simple.

You see —

So then you plot the arc of where that star is visible at that altitude, and where it intersects with the first arc —

Vega will be 23°6' above the horizon at 7:53 P.M. on July 8th only along a specific arc of the Earth's surface. We measure the angle with the sextant, and make note of the time —

Oh, it's 8!

DANG DANG
DANG DANG
DANG DANG
DANG DANG

Then you look up the angle and the time for that star in the almanac . . .

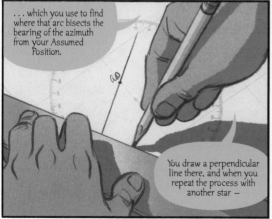

. . . which you use to find where that arc bisects the bearing of the azimuth from your Assumed Position.

You draw a perpendicular line there, and when you repeat the process with another star —

Ergh, I'm afraid it's a lost cause.

Luckily we aren't lacking for navigators on this ship.

SPLASH

40

41

WIND'S BACKING, SOR!

FURL MAINS'L

You too, adaptable helper.

43

On 15 July we crossed the Equator, and enacted the time-honoured tradition of Crossing the Line with all pomp and ceremony.

Neptune, in the person of Chief Petty Officer Evans, hailed and stopped the ship.

He and his motley company solemnly processed to meet Lieutenant Evans.

The barrister read an address to the captain, and made him a member of the Most Ancient Order of Flying Fish.

Those who had not yet Crossed the Line were presented to Neptune for initiation.

Nelson was the first victim.

He was examined by the doctor ...

... given a pill and a dose ...

... and handed over to the barber ...

... who shaved him with a great wooden razor.

Then he was tipped into the bath –

– where the bears were waiting.

45

YOU MISSED GRAN!
But I have goed south!
Not in a British ship!

They tipped him in and wished they had never caught him.

Neptune presented certificates to those who had been initiated, and the proceedings closed with a sing-song in the evening.

The expedition was very fond of singing, though there was hardly anybody in it who could sing.

The usual custom was that every one had to contribute a song in turn all round the table.

If he could not sing, he had to compose a limerick.

If he could not compose a limerick he had to contribute a fine towards the wine fund ...

... which was to make some much-discussed purchases when we reached Cape Town.

At other times we played the most childish games, over which we laughed till we cried.

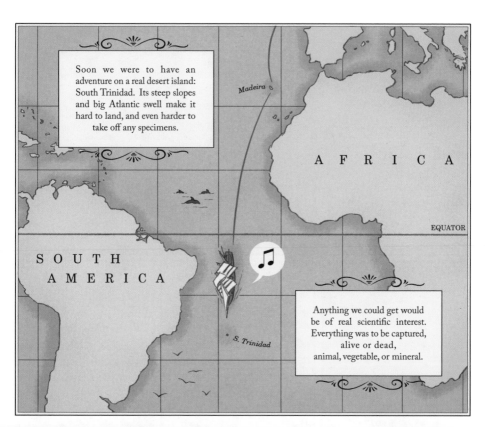

Soon we were to have an adventure on a real desert island: South Trinidad. Its steep slopes and big Atlantic swell make it hard to land, and even harder to take off any specimens.

Anything we could get would be of real scientific interest. Everything was to be captured, alive or dead, animal, vegetable, or mineral.

The sea being comparatively smooth, everybody was landed dry.

Each party was given a particular scientific interest to investigate.

Dr. Atkinson stayed with a sick seaman who had come ashore for some exercise.

Bill, Pennell, and I were on ornithology, collecting birds – and anything else we might find in the process – for the British Museum.

Oh now this is interesting –

– These were supposed to be two separate species.

Sorry!

It might not be so bad to be stranded on a desert island, after all.

Plenty of birds to watch ...

... and crabs to eat.

Surf's come up, quite a lot.

Well. This'll be fun.

Right, let's depot this stuff here so it doesn't get —

Let's depot it up there.

While
we're
waiting?

We skinned through the night, trying to save as many as possible of the bird skins which had been procured.

I don't mind telling you, Bill, I had some bad cramp waiting to swim out to the boat.

I didn't really want that biscuit.

So did I.

We had lost all the eggs, and the guns were dented and rusty, but considering what the birds had been through, the result was not as disappointing as we had expected.

Soon after leaving South Trinidad, we were into seas which were rather different than the ones through which we'd come . . .

62

Give the jam a wind, Marie!

How many for seconds?

Shall I be mother?

Mind your tea there

Whos

Mm, hot

Where's the sugar now?

Push along the butter!

Is this yours?

Any milk left?

Cheers, Hooper old chap!

After you with the coffee?

STAND BY FOR A STEADY!

STEADY!!

STEADY IT IS, SIR!

ONE, TWO, THREE, STEADY!

When are you going to get round to painting these?

Well, I hope to have the Grouse Report ready to send in from Cape Town, so probably after that.

That's a long time to remember the colours.

That's what the notes are for.

It's just practice and discipline, like anything else.

How did you get to be so good at drawing, Bill?

Gentlemen . . . Grace.

WE ARE THE SISTERS
WOT WON THE PRIZE,
THE SISTERS HARDBAKE
WITH THE GOO-GOO EYES!
MY NAME IS GERTRUDE,
AND MINE IS ROSE,
WE SHAN'T BE SINGLE LONG,
I DON'T SUPPOSE!

Have a seat, Bowers.

It's taken.

'S alright, I'll eat standing up.

hould put on
e pianola

You fellows look like ants
from all the way up here!

Didn't the *Waratah*
disappear around here?

I never thought I'd s
but I'm getting tir
of champagne.

Cheers, mate

Anyone seen my spoon?

Any more potatoes?

ly three weeks late

Shall we open another bottle?

Jon my reach . . .

That is of cou
great injust
the current s

ape Town
e war

No, bread in Norway
is lots better.

enough of salt
y, thank you.

Thanks, old sport.

After you with
the mustard, Silas.

This is precisely

After two months at sea, working and living
like sardines in a tin, scientists and sailors were
knitting together as a crew.

The inevitable nicknames had begun to stick.

The Terra Nova was Scott's ship, so in his absence he was known as "The Owner."

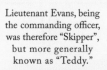

Lieutenant Evans, being the commanding officer, was therefore "Skipper", but more generally known as "Teddy."

Campbell had gone from "Mr. Mate" to "The Wicked Mate."

Pennell was "Penelope."

"Birdie" Bowers

"Marie" Nelson

Atkinson became "Atch" –

and Oates "Titus."

When they were together – which was always – they were "Max and Climax."

"Silas" Wright

"Sunny Jim" Simpson

... and "Uncle Bill" Wilson.

69

CAPE TOWN
SOUTH AFRICA

We finally reached South Africa on 16 August, and smartened up for the occasion.

Captain Scott was in Pretoria when we arrived, but we had a warm welcome from HMS *Pandora* and *Mutine*, which sent us many essentials.

They also sent parties to do maintenance for us, releasing us for a certain amount of freedom on shore, which was appreciated after nine weeks at sea.

A few of us went out to Wynberg, which Oates knew well, having been invalided there when his leg was shattered in the war. He told me later how he had thought he would bleed to death. The man who lay next to him was convinced he had a bullet in the middle of his brain – he could feel it wobbling about in there!

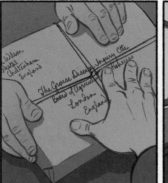

But mostly, we enjoyed our holiday.

Wilson was sent ahead of us to Melbourne, to continue Scott's fundraising tour, and to make arrangements with the Australian members who were to join us in New Zealand.

Captain Scott took his place, and assumed command of his eclectic crew for the first time.

How wonderful to see you again, Lashly — how's about another go, eh?

My dear Simpson, I trust you have been getting some good observations already?

Yes, sir.

...positive surfeit ...ceans, sir.

Enjoying yourself, Cherry?

Very much, sir.

Splendid!

Bill speaks very highly of you.

Well done, Lt. Evans.

Thank you, sir!

In future, though, I'd prefer the wardroom to resemble a respectable scientific vessel, and not an anarchists' den.

Yes, sir.

The big swell which prevails in these latitudes is a most inspiring sight.

A moderate roll rings the bell;

DANG

We soon found out just how much the old Terra Push could roll, which gave rise to the saying . . .

a big roll brings out the cook.

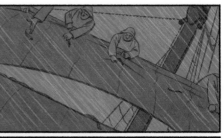

The Roaring Forties soon lived up to their name.

AT LEAST THIS WILL HELP US MAKE UP OUR TIME TO MELBOURNE.

Who ever heard of Easterlies in the Forties?

It doesn't look likely to change, sir, what should we do?

Sail north, as close to the wind as possible. It can't last long.

Scott was impatient – there was much to be done, and not much time.

Meanwhile, while Wilson was away, we enlisted the help of anybody who was interested to help with logging the sea birds.

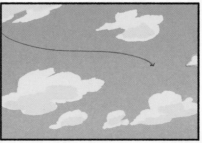

He's so noble ... it seems a shame to kill him.

I'll get the ether, so at least he won't suffer.

I think we were all missing Wilson.

The fair weather released us to bring our plans for Antarctica into more definite shape.

It had been decided to leave New Zealand at an earlier date than had been attempted by any previous expedition, in order to penetrate the pack ice sooner and make an early start laying depots for the next year.

Scott was putting more and more trust in Campbell, who was to lead the Eastern Party.

These six men would be landed in King Edward VII Land, with the task of exploring that unknown territory.

He was also beginning to appreciate Bowers' head for figures and prodigious memory, and recruited him to the Main Party.

This would be based on Ross Island, and from this base the attempt on the Pole would be made next year.

In anticipation of that, a string of depots was to be laid as soon as we arrived, stocking our route with food and supplies.

Birdie knew our inventory down to the last ounce, so would be an invaluable asset.

For our own part, though Scott was a very different leader to Teddy, we began to see his tremendous capacity for planning, his appreciation of talents, and why the Discovery men chose to follow him South again.

The wind then shifted to the south, and we got a small taste of what was awaiting us in the Antarctic ...

FEWEEE

[reef lower t'gallant]

$$-\frac{GM}{r^2}\hat{r}$$

[All hands to deck]

[lower t'gallant yard]

I don't like how that mast is straining.

IT'S CAUGHT ON SOMETHING, SIR!

PERMISSION TO SEE TO IT, SORR!

PERMISSION DENIED, CREAN, IT'S NOT WORTH THE RISK.

We've had every wind but westerly, Campbell, I can't account for it.

Sir?

Sigh.

Raise steam.

We must make up our time to Melbourne.

By the early morning of 12 October, Cape Otway light was in sight.

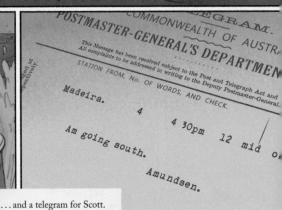

MELBOURNE
AUSTRALIA

Bill came out to meet us from Melbourne, bringing the wives, our mail ...

... and a telegram for Scott.

COMMONWEALTH OF AUSTRA
EGRAM.
POSTMASTER-GENERAL'S DEPARTMEN

This Message has been received subject to the Post and Telegraph Act and
All complaints to be addressed in writing to the Deputy Postmaster-General.

STATION FROM, No. OF WORDS, AND CHECK.

Madeira.   4   4 30pm   12 mid o

Am going south.

Amundsen.

ROALD AMUNDSEN

Captain Roald Amundsen was one of the most notable of living explorers, and was in the prime of life – thirty-eight years old, four years younger than Scott.

He had been in the Antarctic before Scott, with the Belgica Expedition in 1897-99, the first expedition to overwinter there, and therefore did not consider the South Pole in any sense our property.

The *Belgica*, trapped in ice ▶

Since then, he had realized the dream of centuries of exploration by passing through the North-West Passage, in 1905.

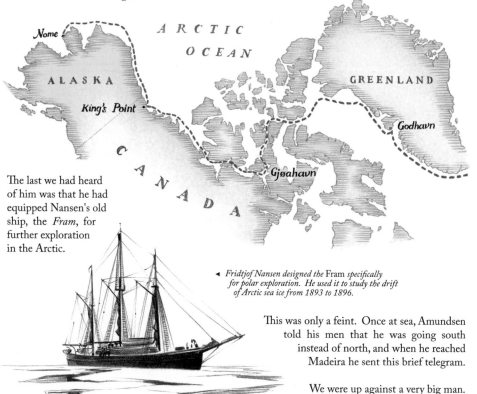

ARCTIC OCEAN

Nome

ALASKA

King's Point

GREENLAND

Godhavn

CANADA

Gjøahavn

The last we had heard of him was that he had equipped Nansen's old ship, the *Fram*, for further exploration in the Arctic.

◀ *Fridtjof Nansen designed the* Fram *specifically for polar exploration. He used it to study the drift of Arctic sea ice from 1893 to 1896.*

This was only a feint. Once at sea, Amundsen told his men that he was going south instead of north, and when he reached Madeira he sent this brief telegram.

We were up against a very big man.

[What are Amundsen's plans?]

Christiania.   2   9 13 pm   7 m

Unknown.

Nansen.

RGS London.   9   11 45 pm   9 mid ob

Accessed charts of Ross Sea some months ago.

Keltie.

The rest of us enjoyed the best Melbourne had to offer.

Wilson rejoined the ship in Melbourne, and Scott left her, to arrange further business matters and rejoin us in New Zealand.

By that time, I think Scott had seen enough of the personnel of the expedition to be able to pass a fair judgment upon them.

I can only think that he was pleased.

Such enthusiasm and comradeship as prevailed on board could bear only good fruit.

It would certainly have been possible to find a body of men who could work a sailing ship with greater skill, but not men who were more willing, and, in the midst of considerable discomfort, to work hard at distasteful jobs and be always cheerful.

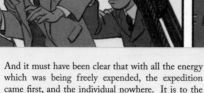

And it must have been clear that with all the energy which was being freely expended, the expedition came first, and the individual nowhere. It is to the honour of all concerned that from the time it left to the time it returned, this spirit always prevailed.

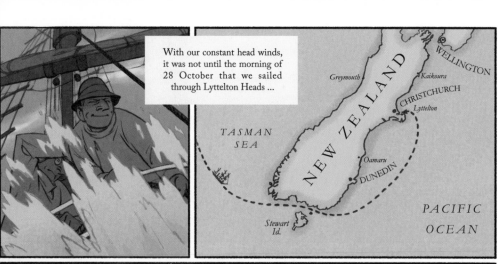

With our constant head winds, it was not until the morning of 28 October that we sailed through Lyttelton Heads ...

TASMAN SEA

NEW ZEALAND

WELLINGTON

Greymouth

Kaikoura

CHRISTCHURCH

Lyttelton

Oamaru

DUNEDIN

Stewart Id.

PACIFIC OCEAN

The word had gone forth that we would sail away at the end of November. This was our last rendez-vous with civiliza-tion, and everything we might need on the ice had to be carefully considered here, before we left.

Bowers oversaw the unloading of the ship, and carefully counted every item into Shed No. 5., which has been put at the disposal of so many Antarctic expeditions.

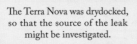

The Terra Nova was drydocked, so that the source of the leak might be investigated.

This remedied, she needed only a fraction of the pumping that had been necessary hitherto – to the great relief of all.

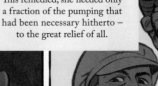

It was found to originate at the stern, where a bolt hole had been left unfilled.

The dogs and ponies for the Expedition had been selected in Russia by Mr. Cecil H. Meares, an adventurous type who had spent several winters fur-trapping in Siberia, and was to be our dog expert in the South. He had already had an adventure shipping the animals down through the tropics to meet us here.

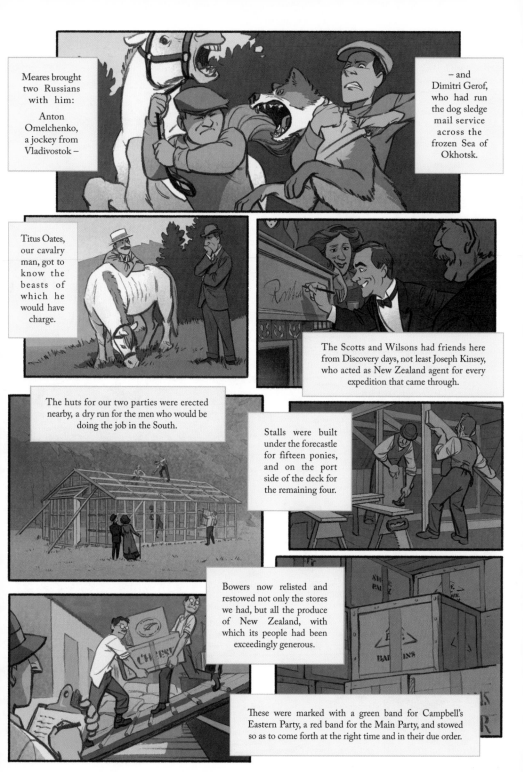

Meares brought two Russians with him:

Anton Omelchenko, a jockey from Vladivostok –

– and Dimitri Gerof, who had run the dog sledge mail service across the frozen Sea of Okhotsk.

Titus Oates, our cavalry man, got to know the beasts of which he would have charge.

The Scotts and Wilsons had friends here from Discovery days, not least Joseph Kinsey, who acted as New Zealand agent for every expedition that came through.

The huts for our two parties were erected nearby, a dry run for the men who would be doing the job in the South.

Stalls were built under the forecastle for fifteen ponies, and on the port side of the deck for the remaining four.

Bowers now relisted and restowed not only the stores we had, but all the produce of New Zealand, with which its people had been exceedingly generous.

These were marked with a green band for Campbell's Eastern Party, a red band for the Main Party, and stowed so as to come forth at the right time and in their due order.

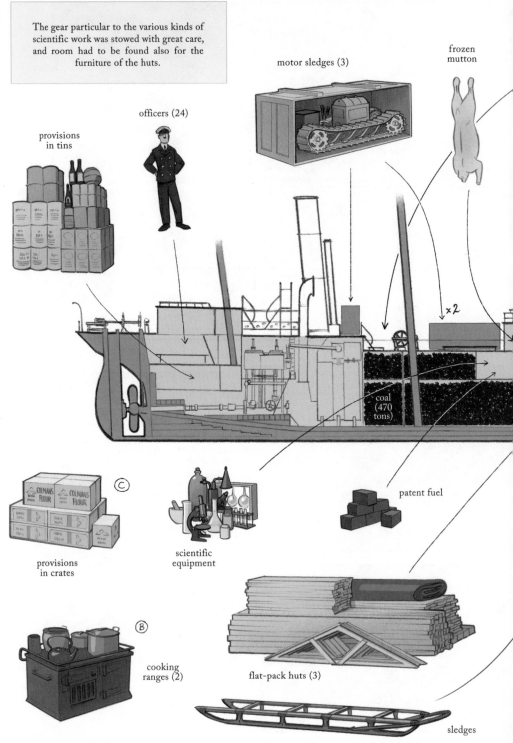

The gear particular to the various kinds of scientific work was stowed with great care, and room had to be found also for the furniture of the huts.

motor sledges (3)

frozen mutton

officers (24)

provisions in tins

×2

coal (470 tons)

Ⓒ

patent fuel

provisions in crates

scientific equipment

Ⓑ

cooking ranges (2)

flat-pack huts (3)

sledges

coal in sacks (30 tons)

dogs (34)

ponies (19)

petrol

pony fodder

crew (41)

extra pony fodder

Ⓑ

Ⓒ

electrical wire

Ⓑ

travelling gear

Ⓐ

hut furnishings

extra cloth

sewing machine

Ⓑ

beds & bedding

The Terra Nova was a great consumer of coal: the length of the ship's stay in the South, and the amount of exploration she could do after landing the shore parties, depended almost entirely on how much coal she could be persuaded to hold after all the necessities of modern scientific exploration had been wedged tightly into her.

Also added to the ship were several new crew members.

T. Griffith Taylor, senior geologist and physiographer, had been friends with Wright at Cambridge, and they had applied for the expedition together.

His fellow Australian and junior geologist, Frank Debenham, was the student and recommendation of Prof. Edgworth David, who had been south with Shackleton.

Raymond Priestley was the geologist for Campbell's party, and would be applying his expertise to King Edward VII Land.

Bernard Day was our engineer, in whose loving care were placed the three experimental motor sledges.

And Herbert Ponting, world traveller and expedition photo...

CAMERA ARTIST!

As the time of departure drew near, each day of civilization grew more and more precious.

But before we knew it . . .

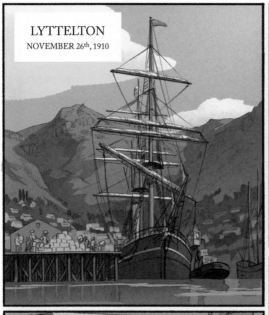

LYTTELTON
NOVEMBER 26th, 1910

Everyone aft!

The bishop will be here soon!

SHA-
SPLOOSH

GET THAT MAN OFF THIS SHIP!

See to it that Petty Officer Evans has a bed for the night and have him join us in Dunedin.

What's that banner say?

" Excursions to the Heads, one shilling."

STAND BY TO SWING SHIP!

Mr Taylor, you haven't got a knife on you, have you?

ARRR!

Take it away, please, it'll influence the compass.

Two days later, we did it all again ...

While the Terra Nova was being topped up with coal at Port Chalmers, we were invited to a gala sendoff in Dunedin.

PORT CHALMERS
November 29th, 1910

One last time we made
a festive departure.

Three cheers
for Captain Scott!

103

One last time, we were seen off by an armada of well-wishers.

One last time our friends and relations took the harbour tug back to shore.

See you in 1912.

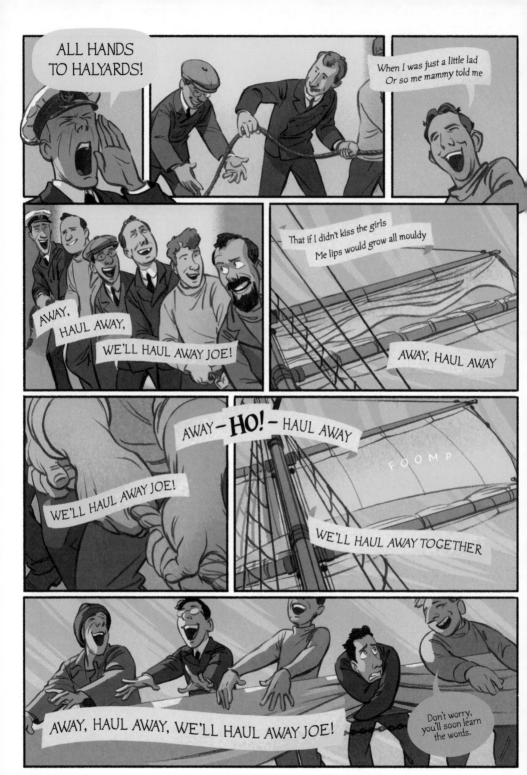

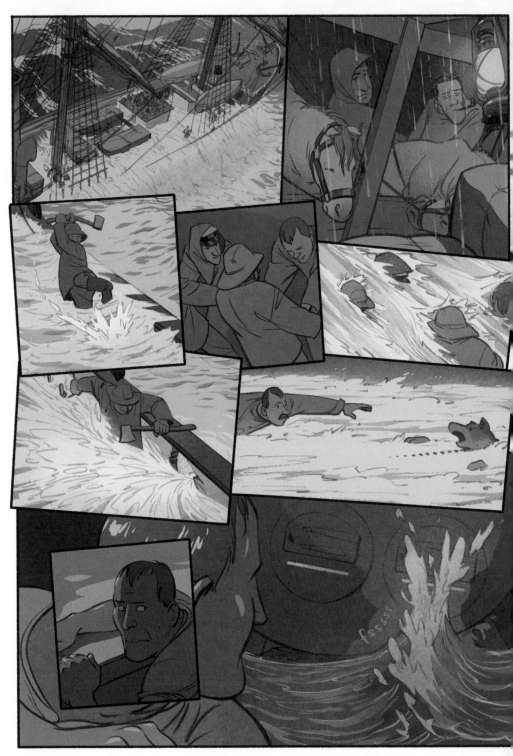

SHOOMP

pff

We've drawn down the fires –

– but the boiler is still hot, and if the water reaches it, we risk permanent damage, if not an explosion.

Can one get into the pump shaft to unclog it?

Only through the after hatch.

SHOOMP

Is there another way?

If we open that, we won't be afloat ten minutes.

We can move the coal.

Can you get through the bulkhead?

Nearest is from the engine room, but there's an iron bulkhead and a few tons of coal in the way.

It'll take some time, but should do.

Evans, we need time. Get all available hands on a bucket chain.

Right.

Sir.

Has an 800-ton ship ever been bailed out with buckets before?

This storm wants to save us a lot of trouble and two years of work, Campbell.

I'd rather it didn't.

Now I'm going to see a man about a horse.

117

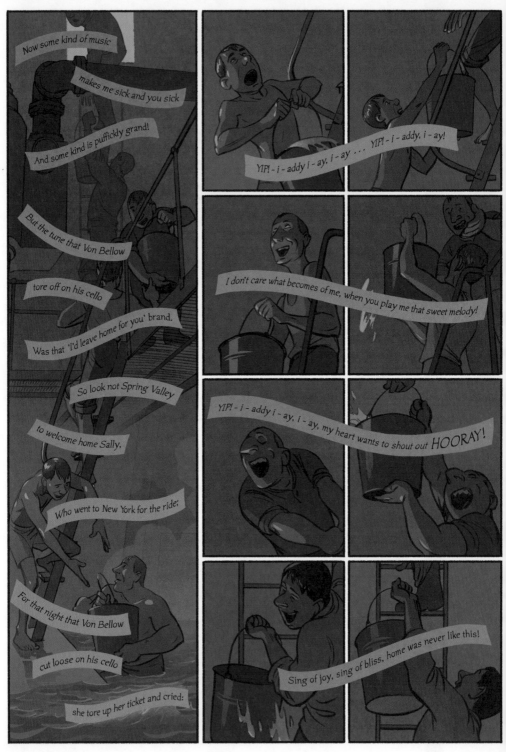

TUG
TUG

We were by no means out of the wood, but by
the end of the second day, things began to improve.

SCRRRRPP

The worst of the storm past, we were able to put things right and take stock.

Oh there you are, Ponting.

HURK!!

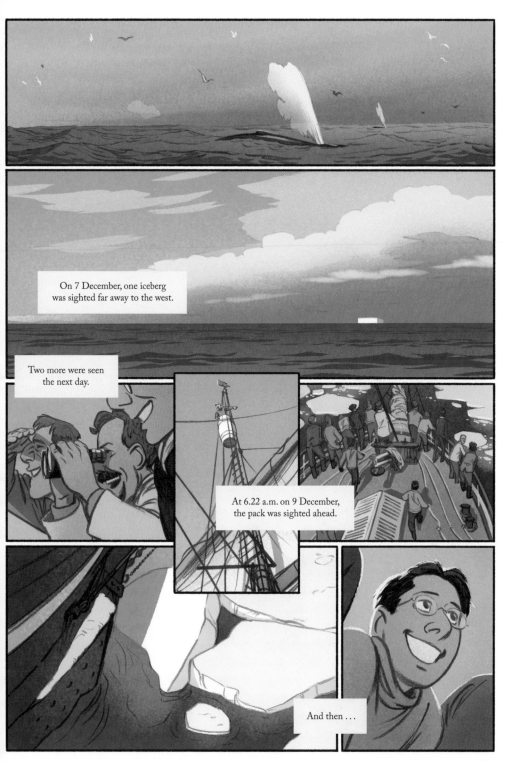

On 7 December, one iceberg was sighted far away to the west.

Two more were seen the next day.

At 6.22 a.m. on 9 December, the pack was sighted ahead.

And then . . .

WHAT IS THE PACK?

Speaking very generally, it is the ice which forms on the sea during the winter, and is blown northwards by the southerly blizzards.

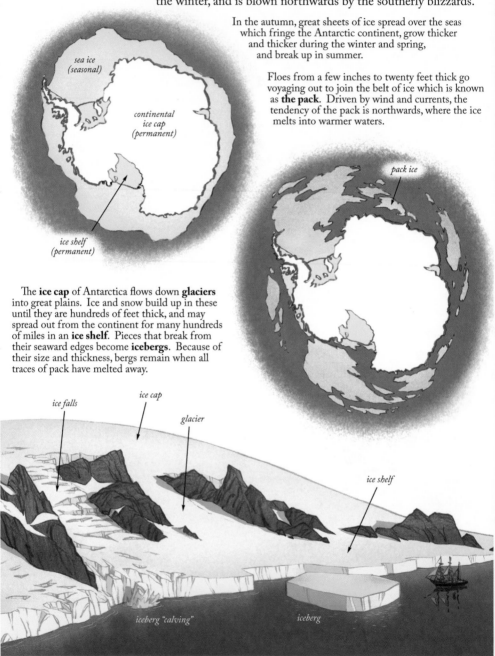

sea ice
(seasonal)

continental
ice cap
(permanent)

ice shelf
(permanent)

In the autumn, great sheets of ice spread over the seas which fringe the Antarctic continent, grow thicker and thicker during the winter and spring, and break up in summer.

Floes from a few inches to twenty feet thick go voyaging out to join the belt of ice which is known as **the pack**. Driven by wind and currents, the tendency of the pack is northwards, where the ice melts into warmer waters.

pack ice

The **ice cap** of Antarctica flows down **glaciers** into great plains. Ice and snow build up in these until they are hundreds of feet thick, and may spread out from the continent for many hundreds of miles in an **ice shelf**. Pieces that break from their seaward edges become **icebergs**. Because of their size and thickness, bergs remain when all traces of pack have melted away.

ice falls

ice cap

glacier

ice shelf

iceberg "calving"

iceberg

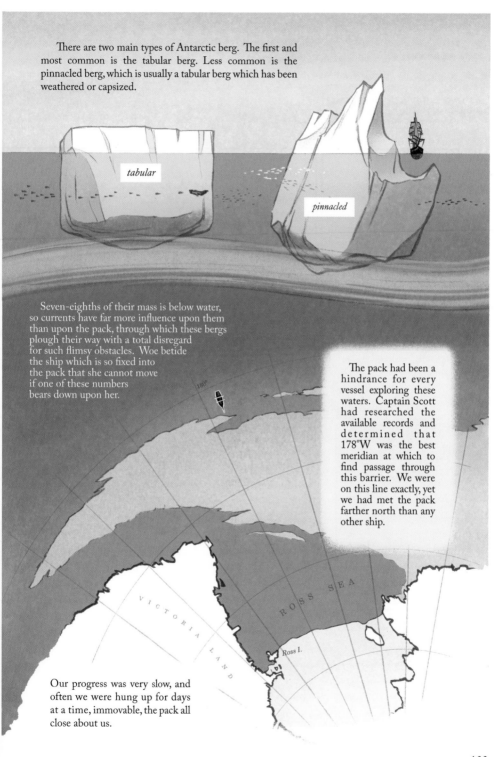

There are two main types of Antarctic berg. The first and most common is the tabular berg. Less common is the pinnacled berg, which is usually a tabular berg which has been weathered or capsized.

tabular

pinnacled

Seven-eighths of their mass is below water, so currents have far more influence upon them than upon the pack, through which these bergs plough their way with a total disregard for such flimsy obstacles. Woe betide the ship which is so fixed into the pack that she cannot move if one of these numbers bears down upon her.

The pack had been a hindrance for every vessel exploring these waters. Captain Scott had researched the available records and determined that 178°W was the best meridian at which to find passage through this barrier. We were on this line exactly, yet we had met the pack farther north than any other ship.

180°

VICTORIA LAND

ROSS SEA

Ross I.

Our progress was very slow, and often we were hung up for days at a time, immovable, the pack all close about us.

Most of us were more than happy to get off the ship and stretch our legs.

And then, without warning and reason, it would open out again, and we would make just a few more miles.

As time went on this waiting in the pack became almost intolerable. Every day in the pack was one we couldn't spend laying depots for next year.

And all the time our scanty supply of coal was being eaten up ...

Delay was always irksome to Scott.

... until it was said that Campbell's party would never be taken to King Edward VII Land.

Patience and always more patience!

To the rest of us, the pack was a land of enchantment, and we scarce wanted to sleep lest we miss some new wonder.

To make progress through the pack, sometimes it was a matter of forcing two floes apart, at others of charging and breaking one.

Bowers became famous for the way in which he put the ship at the ice.

135

BOWERS!

Sorry!

None of us whose privilege it was to be there will forget our first sight of the penguins. They are extraordinarily like children, or like old men, full of their own importance and late for dinner.

She has rings on her fingers, and bells on her toes,
And she shall have music wherever she goes!

God Save Our Gracious King
Long Live Our Noble King
God Save The King!

To the biologist, the pack is of absorbing interest.

If you want to see life, naked and unashamed, study the struggles of this ice-world, from the diatom in the ice-floe to the big killer whale; each stage essential to the life of the stage above, and living on the stage below.

The PROTOPLASMIC CYCLE
by T. Griffith Taylor

Big floes have little floes all around about 'em.
And all the yellow diatoms couldn't do without 'em ...

While up above the Afterguard attack them on the floe:

Forty million shrimplets
feed upon the latter,

Along comes the Orca and kills these down below,

And they make the penguin and the seals and whales much fatter.

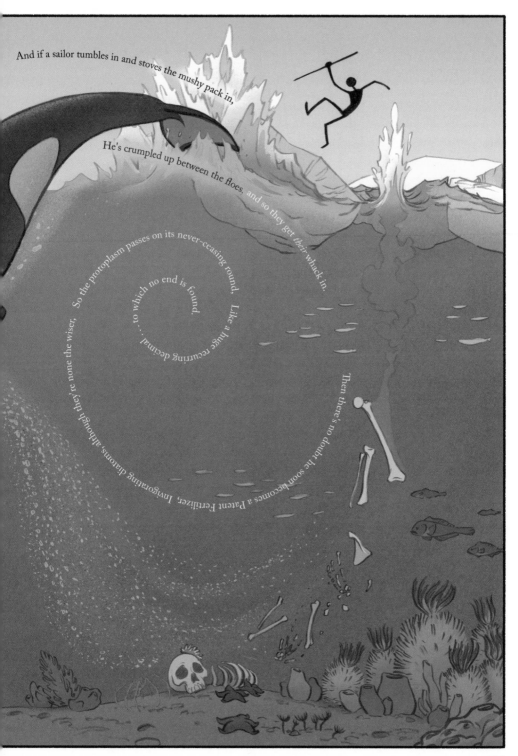

And if a sailor tumbles in and stoves the mushy pack in,

He's crumpled up between the floes, and so they get *their* whack in.

So the protoplasm passes on its never-ceasing round, Like a huge recurring decimal ..... to which no end is found.

....although they're none the wiser, Invigorating diatoms, a Patent Fertilizer, Then there's no doubt he soon becomes

139

Once, it had been suggested that we might spend Christmas in our hut. Then the hope was at least to clear the pack by then.

But on Christmas Eve, there was still no end in sight.

Bill?

Come on up.

Here we go!

Once in royal David's city,
In a lowly cattle shed . . .

Where a mother laid her baby,
In a manger for its bed.

Mary was that mother mild,
Jesus Christ her little child.

He came down
to earth from heaven,
Who is God, and Lord of all,
And his shelter was a stable,
And his cradle was a stall.

With the poor, and mean and lowly,

Lived on Earth our sa-a-viour

ho . . .

ly

AHA !

Is three enough for Christmas dinner, do you think?

You take those back to the ship, I'll get one or two more.

Best to collect as many juvenile skins as we can while we're still in the pack.

Happy hunting!

WOOOOUUUUUUUUU

wou wou WOU

wou

wou

wou

wou

143

145

On the 28th of December, there were signs of open water ahead.

It was decided to raise steam.

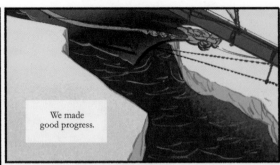

We made good progress.

Hour by hour it became more obvious that we neared the open sea.

At the close of the year, we left the ice behind.

I turned in, thinking to wake in 1911.

146

But I had not been long asleep when –

Cherry!

Have you seen the land?

Wrap your blankets round you, and come and see.

All the high lights are snow lit up by the sun.

HAPPY NEW YEAR!

ANNOTATIONS

Welcome to the Annotations, repository of sources, explanations, and amusing anecdotes that didn't make it into the comic. I've tried to stay as true to the history as possible, but sometimes the history is a little too bloated or confusing, and narrative flow demands some streamlining of chronology and details. My changes have been minor and inconsequential, but this is where I flag them and tell you what really happened, so you'll be in no doubt as to what's history and what's storytelling.

The original *Worst Journey in the World* is a first-hand account written less than ten years after the events, drawn from the author's own journals and memories, as well as the letters and journals of his colleagues. As such, it is a good source, but cross-referencing with other viewpoints is always valuable, and I have used many other accounts to flesh out what's in Cherry's book. For simplicity, sources I refer to frequently are noted with a letter code and page number only. The letter codes are as follows:

ACG – Cherry's journals
BAE – Miscellaneous papers of the British Antarctic Expedition 1910, held at the Scott Polar Research Institute (SPRI). Mostly I am referring to the first two volumes of seven, which are Atkinson's unpublished account of the Expedition.
CSW – Wright's journals and memoir, published as *Silas*
Deb – Debenham's journals, published as *The Quiet Land*
EAW – Wilson's journals
HRB – Bowers' journals and/or letters
RFS – *Scott's Last Expedition*, Vol.1; the expedition journals of Robert Falcon Scott
Seaver's *Bowers* – *'Birdie' Bowers of the Antarctic*, by George Seaver
Seaver's *Wilson* – *Edward Wilson of the Antarctic*, by George Seaver
SLE2 – *Scott's Last Expedition*, Vol.2; reports by various members of the Expedition
SWS – *South With Scott*, by Edward R.G.R. Evans
WJ – *The Worst Journey in the World*, by Apsley Cherry-Gararrd
WJ:PS – Postscript to *Worst Journey*, written by Cherry-Garrard in 1948
    and published in the 1951 edition of *Worst Journey*
WS:TSL – *With Scott: The Silver Lining*, by T. Griffith Taylor

Less frequent sources are given their full title in their first citation and then referred to by author's surname thereafter. If a citation is marked "ed," that means I have edited the wording. You can look up the original to decide whether I went too far.

A full bibliography and list of suggested reading appears at the end.

PROLOGUE

The idea for this prologue came from a recurring dream Cherry had, in which the Polar Party walks into the hut at Cape Evans, "shaking the snow from their clothes and the ice from their faces … The disappointment of finding that it is only a dream will last for days." [Cherry-Garrard, foreword to Seaver's *Wilson*, xii] Later in his life, Cherry was consumed by the idea that, had he pushed a few days south from One Ton Depot where he was waiting in March of 1912, he might have met the Polar Party and saved them from their fate. I have mashed the two ideas into one thwarted wish-fulfilment dream.

1. WJ xvii

PAGE 1

2. I had been told the air in Antarctica is so dry you don't get breath clouds, or even steam off your cocoa. Then I went myself, and saw with my own eyes steam coming off my cocoa, but I admit there wasn't much in the way of breath clouds. They evoke the

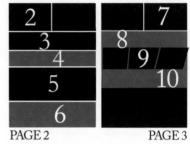

PAGE 2　　　　　　　　　PAGE 3

sound of dogs' panting, though, and show the cold, and dreams are exempt from atmospheric physics anyway, so the breath clouds stay.

3. Cherry is wearing *finneskoe*, as they did when travelling over snow. These are traditional footwear of the Sámi people of northern Scandinavia, and are made from reindeer skin, with the fur lying both ways on the sole of the foot to help with traction. The boot is soft and fits loosely, which allows one's foot to flex and encourages circulation, keeping it warm. The expedition brought hundreds of finneskoe to Antarctica but found many of them poor quality; in some cases they barely lasted a month. [BAE]

4. The narration through the Prologue is gleaned from the introduction to *Worst Journey*, and its closing chapter, as well as the Postscript which Cherry wrote in 1948. Page numbers refer to my 1951 edition which has all three. This line is from the closing chapter. [WJ 575]

5. These snow features are called *sastrugi*, which are a different thing from snowdrifts. Drifts are deposits of blown snow, and face away from prevailing winds; sastrugi are carved by the wind, and face toward it.

6. WJ 575

7. The wheel here is a sledgemeter. It measures the distance a sledge has travelled. If the sledge driver knows how far he's gone, in which compass direction, he can estimate his position on the map by a process called "dead reckoning." Usually, dead reckoning was a backup to proper celestial navigation – calculating one's location using the position of the sun – but some sledge drivers were bad at maths and never learned how to do that.

8. WJ:PS 601

9. On a sunny day, riding on a rushing dog sledge, Cherry would almost certainly have been wearing snow goggles, but they rather get in the way of facial expressions.

10. WJ:PS 603, ed.

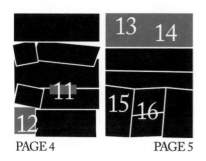

PAGE 4   PAGE 5

11, 12. WJ:PS 603, ed.

13. WJ 543

14. WJ 547, ed.

15. This harks to something that actually did happen. On the way back from laying depots, early in the Expedition, one of the two dog teams broke through the lid of a crevasse. They very luckily escaped plunging into the depths, but it was a salutary lesson in why dog teams are not safe on crevassed ice. The incident influenced Scott's decision not to take dogs up the Beardmore Glacier to the Pole, which he had previously been planning to do. You'll find out more about this in Vol.2, but if you want to read ahead, see WJ 124-127.

16. I spent years trying to find out how one used the *tui* stick to brake a sledge, just for these two panels. The most helpful source ended up being a silly doodle by Teddy Evans which Cherry had stuck in one of his diaries. Bless the archives at SPRI.

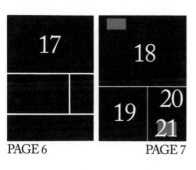

PAGE 6   PAGE 7

17. On the Beardmore Glacier, they crossed crevasses which were described as Regent Street (a wide street in London with tall buildings either side) and big enough to lower the *Terra Nova* into without touching the sides. They dropped an empty oil can down one and never heard it hit bottom.

18. A photo of Lamer House appears in Sara Wheeler's *Cherry*. I have taken the liberty of adding a wall and gate where it may not have had one (there was a gate round the side). This house burned down in 1951, four years after Cherry sold it to move to London. The new Lamer House is built on the foundation of the old, and you can see it from a lovely walking path between Wheathampstead and Shaw's Corner in Ayot St Lawrence, if you are in Hertfordshire and looking for something to do.

19. I have not been able to find any good photos of the Lamer library, so I have based Cherry's library on that of Anglesey Abbey, with some adjustments to fit the description of Lamer given by Wheeler.

20. According to Wheeler, Cherry actually wrote *Worst Journey* paragraph by paragraph on index cards, which he then arranged and handed off to a typist. That's far too complicated to communicate in a simple prologue, though, whereas everyone understands a typewriter.

21. WJ vii

22. A perk of working so much in the archives is that I can put real documents on Cherry's desk. The little book wedged under the typewriter on the previous page is his diary for the ship journey down. This booklet is a standard sledging diary – everyone used roughly the same make. The envelopes at upper

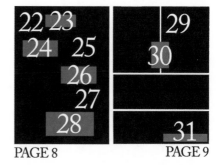

PAGE 8   PAGE 9

right were made for the expedition, with the crest on the flap. The two books are the 1913 edition of *Scott's Last Expedition*, Volumes 1 and 2.

23. WJ viii, paraphrased for archaic language

24. WJ v

25. Ponting's photo of Bowers, Wilson, and Cherry about to head off on the Winter Journey.

26. WJ vi

27. One real document and one imaginary one: On top is a hypothetical letter from Kathleen Scott, whose handwriting really is this swishy. Underneath is the letter Atkinson sent from Hut Point, asking Cherry to go meet the Polar Party at One Ton Depot in his place, the significance of which you will understand later.

28. WJ lxiii – Cherry is glossing over some post-expedition drama, here.

29. Another titbit from Wheeler is that Cherry liked to drink dark roast coffee, black.

30. WJ lxiii

31. This line is my invention, to bridge the prologue and the story proper, because Cherry didn't write one for that job. It's true though: I'm spending the next 140 pages on the journey to Antarctica because it's the foundation for a lot of what happened there.

CARDIFF

For a project that is striving for maximum historical accuracy, I'm afraid I've made up most of this opening bit, but it needed to be simplified. The main liberty I've taken is compressing a lot into one day. The *Terra Nova* was overhauled and refitted as a research ship in London, and then sailed to Cardiff, which was to be her home port. Many of the Expedition members joined her at the beginning of June in London, not mid-June in Cardiff, including Bowers, Oates, and Cherry. Wilson did join her on the 14th, in Cardiff, but this was after the grand send-off banquet, not before – the banquet was on the evening of the 13th, not the eve of departure. Wright joined on the 14th as well.

Having everything happen in the right order, here, would have meant at least twice as many pages and a great opportunity for confusion, for no real gain. It was necessary only that people join the ship and you meet some of the central cast, so compressing the departure gets things moving faster. I hope you can forgive me.

1. The glamour shot of the *Terra Nova* is mostly taken off an excellent photograph in the collection of the National Museum of Wales/Amgueddfa Cymru, whose photo library has informed the whole Cardiff chapter immensely.

2. There has been a significant Somali community in Cardiff, centred on the docks, since the 1880s.

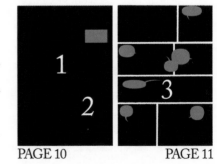

PAGE 10   PAGE 11

3. Bowers was in charge of stores; he was meticulous about where things ought to go and had a perfect memory for where they were stowed. Before he joined the Royal Indian Marine, Bowers served on merchant ships, so had experience with the tricky business of loading cargo, and was praised for making use of every inch of available space.

4. Bowers wrote in a letter to his family, "Silas struck me one day on the ship as a typical Yankee name and in a happy moment I called him Mr. Silas P. Wright of the Philadelphia Educational Seminary. Since then he has never been called anything but Cousin Silas or Silas." [quoted in CSW p.28] Wright, a Canadian, was constantly ribbed for being American. There is a popular song, recorded in 1911, which introduces "Silas P. Hank" as an American expert on how to sing ragtime, so the name may have been in the air around that time.

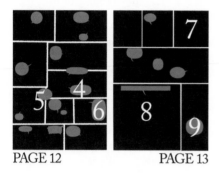

PAGE 12 PAGE 13

5. Wright was studying radiation at Cavendish Labs, where a lot of pioneering early work in particle physics was happening. Both he and his geologist friend T. Griffith Taylor applied to join the Expedition, but only Taylor was accepted. To prove Wright's fitness, and to petition for the decision to be changed, they filled their pockets with hard-boiled eggs and walked from Cambridge to the Expedition's offices in London – 50 miles – in one day. "It was a non-stop effort," wrote Taylor, "and Wright came through 'smiling,' but my feet were so sore that I could hardly stand next day. My chief recollection is one of loathing for hard-boiled eggs, and of the relief with which I dropped three-quarters of our provisions in a secluded corner of King's Cross!" [WS:TSL 7-8] Eggs or no, the feat worked, and Wright was brought on as physicist.

6. This suggestion actually comes via Taylor. [WS:TSL 32] Character introductions are important, and I wanted to establish Silas as a resourceful independent thinker, so I've given it to him. Given that they were such friends, I trust they don't mind sharing.

7. Oates' scruffiness prompted much comment. According to his biographers, this workmanlike appearance, in an era during which society was structured on class and visible markers thereof, "was a deliberate snook cocked at authority and society," and a subversion of his military rank and the rigours of uniform. [Limb & Cordingley, *Captain Oates, Soldier and Explorer*, p.117] Bowers and Oates – who was nicknamed "Farmer Hayseed" for a while – got to be good friends on the voyage, so don't worry too much about them starting on the wrong foot.

8. In the Boer War, Oates' regiment was surrounded and outnumbered. The Boers offered him a chance to surrender, and he gave this notorious reply, which made him a minor celebrity. Had things gone differently, those might have been his most famous words. You can read the details of the event in Limb & Cordingley pp.41-42; the actual event sounds less dramatic than the way it's staged here, but if you think Victorian cartoonists would opt for accuracy in a moment of jingoistic pride, you don't know Victorian cartoonists.

9. As part of the fundraising effort for the Expedition, places were offered to volunteers if they donated £1,000 (the equivalent of £120,458 in 2020). Only Oates and Cherry, both landed gentry, ended up joining under this scheme. Cherry had initially been declined on the grounds of his eyesight, but decided to make the donation anyway, which so impressed Scott as to his character that he was given a second chance. [Wheeler, 59]

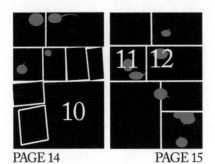

PAGE 14 **PAGE 15**

10. Bowers falling down the hold happened in London (see note 11). As far as I know, no record is made of how it happened; he was not a clumsy person, and blaming someone would have been ungentlemanly. My apologies to Gran for putting it on his shoulders here, but it was such a convenient way to set up Bowers' indestructibility, Gran's occasional thoughtlessness, and some irresistible foreshadowing.

11. "... Lieut. Bowers came home from the Indian Marine to begin his duties as Stores Officer by falling down the main hatch on to the pig iron ballast. ... when Campbell reported the matter, I am reported to have said, 'What a silly ass!' This may have been true, for coming all the way from Bombay to join us and then immediately falling down the hatch did seem a bit careless. However, when Campbell added that Bowers had not hurt himself my enthusiasm returned and I said, 'What a splendid fellow!' Bowers fell nineteen feet without injuring himself in the slightest." [SWS 21]

12. This line comes from Frank Debenham's charming memoir *In the Antarctic* (p.134) where it refers to Wilson's arrival at the ship in New Zealand, not Cardiff.

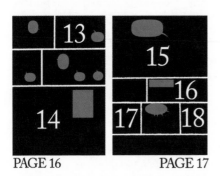

PAGE 16 **PAGE 17**

13. Mrs. Oriana F. Wilson was a wonderful character, and I sincerely regret that I don't have more room for her in this book. We'll just have to make the most of the moments we do get, as indeed we should in life generally.

14. I traced this off a photo I took of the Royal Hotel when I visited Cardiff in 2017. About two hours after finishing the drawing, I found a photo from 1910 which shows the hotel with more chimneys and a clock face. You may supply these with your imagination if you wish.

15. What is now the "Captain Scott Room" at the Royal Hotel is not, in fact, the room in which the farewell banquet was held, but a floor above it. It is, however, the room you can visit and photograph. I have invented the ceiling (the modern one is plain and boxy, to cover ventilation ducts) but the rest is as you'll find it. In the panelling behind the head of the table there is now a small case with Expedition relics.

16. "One old chap who gave five hundred pounds ended up the evening by walking (with assistance) down the centre of the table." [CSW 8]

17. "At Scott's invitation Seaman Evans was invited to say a few words. He took the opportunity to praise the leadership of Capt. Scott and make it clear that no one else could have persuaded him to return to the Antarctic." [Anthony M. Johnson, *Scott of the Antarctic and Cardiff*, p.29]

18. Lt. Evans' party trick was lifting a man by the belt or seat of his trousers with his teeth. It originated in his midshipman days, and he carried on doing it well into the 1920s at least. There is no record of it happening at the farewell dinner in Cardiff, but there is also no record of it *not* happening, and it's too good to leave out. [Reginald Pound, *Evans of the Broke*, pp.17, 27, 46, and 190]

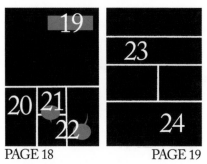

PAGE 18   PAGE 19

19. WJ 1, ed.

20.   Scott bought the *Terra Nova* from a whaling company and registered her as a private yacht, which is why in her expedition years she is officially the *Terra Nova* R.Y.S. (Royal Yacht Squadron). They got dispensation to fly the White Ensign, the flag of the Royal Navy, perhaps on account of Scott's prestige in his naval life and the number of Navy men sailing with them. It was not officially a Naval expedition, as many polar expeditions of the past had been, but it was run on Naval lines and respected Naval hierarchies, so might as well have been. The Naval legacy – and the disparity of mindset between the Navy men and their civilian colleagues – is an important part of understanding both how the expedition ran, and what went wrong.

21.   The *Terra Nova* actually flew the Welsh flag from her mizzenmast, above the White Ensign, and the flag of the City of Cardiff on the foremast. Given that there are probably people living in Cardiff who wouldn't recognise the City flag, I have given that place to the Welsh one which has slightly more recognition. The modern flag has the dragon on all fours, but in 1910 it was standing. If you don't believe me, you can find the actual flag taken on the *Terra Nova* at the National Museum of Wales/Amgueddfa Cymru.

22.   As the shamrock is to Ireland and the thistle to Scotland, so the leek is the emblem of Wales. This exchange comes from Teddy's memoir *South With Scott*, p. 26: "Some wag pointed to the flag and asked why we had not a leek under it, and I felt bound to reply that we had a leak in the fore peak!" We will hear more of the leak shortly.

23.   Most of industrial Cardiff is gone now, but the Pierhead Building – that red castle-ish thing to the left of the *Terra Nova* – still stands proud on the waterfront, and the *Terra Nova*'s compass lives inside.

24.   The sail-past of the Dreadnoughts actually occurred on the journey from London to Cardiff, but it was too good not to rearrange for my purposes. Bowers described it thus:

> I must say I was never so impressed in my life with hideous strength. The new monsters are ugliness itself, but for sheer diabolical brutality in ship-building some of the Dreadnought cruisers take the cake. The look of them is enough to scare anyone, and when you pass close enough to look into the muzzles of their guns the effect is something to be remembered. Much as I love ships, and especially H.M. Ships, there was something about the look of the squadron that was Satanic. The silence and the mist intensified the effect. [Seaver's *Bowers*, 151]

One of the poignant things about this expedition is that it occurred at the turning of an age. Even in 1910 it seemed common knowledge that there was a war on the way; the only question was when and how it would kick off. Our retrospect in full knowledge of how dark and dreadful WWI would prove to be gives the years preceding it the ache of a lost golden afternoon. It's not something that can be covered in the expedition's story (at least not by this storyteller) but missing it out entirely would be to lose a note in the chord.

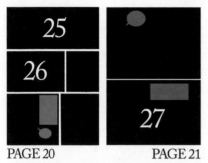

PAGE 20   PAGE 21

25. I have exaggerated the scale of the Dreadnought for dramatic effect, but not by much – the main yard of the *Terra Nova* was level with the big guns, according to Bowers.

26. At a tall ship festival in Vancouver, the juxtaposition of the old-fashioned sailing ships with the container ships I usually saw in the harbour made a deep impression on me. When you see a tall ship in a movie, it's often the biggest thing in the shot, and a ship under full sail is majestically grand. But they looked such tiny frail things sailing next to an average ship of today. Sailing ships were going obsolete in 1910, and wooden ships had been obsolete for fifty years; they were better adapted to polar travel, though, which is why whaling companies, such as the one from which Scott purchased the *Terra Nova*, still used them. (See note 19 on p.201 for more on this.) This encounter with the Dreadnoughts lets me show how much of a throwback *Terra Nova* was – not just technologically, but almost spiritually, being more like Cook's journeys of exploration than contemporary endeavours of territorial conquest and trade. This is a lot for one small drawing to carry. Maybe it doesn't. That's what I was going for, anyway.

27. Just like the looming war, the Empire is another note in the chord. In 1910 it was at its zenith, and would have coloured everyone's perception of the world. The map was a hodgepodge of red patches which denoted British-controlled territory, and the people travelling from one to another would have thought in those terms. (See Francis Spufford, *I May Be Some Time*, p.251 for more on this – for a broader encapsulation of the time and mindset, I recommend reading from p.246.)

Admitting the existence of the Empire makes people uncomfortable now, bound up as it is with oppression and brutality. However, looking at the world through Edwardian eyes, with its red patches, helps one understand the optimism – and, indeed, hubris – with which these adventures were approached. We have conquered most of the world! What could possibly stop us? So many times in my research it has struck me how much the Edwardian Englishman sounds like a modern American: We are the greatest civilisation on Earth; we've got it all figured out; we bring betterment to backward nations; all we need is enough gumption and a positive attitude, and the world will fall at our feet!

… It doesn't always work that way.

NORTH ATLANTIC

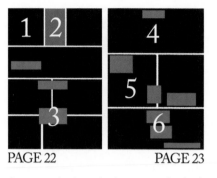

PAGE 22   PAGE 23

1. The instrument being set up here is a device for measuring atmospheric charge. As far as I can deduce from contemporary descriptions of similar instruments, and from the paper which Simpson and Wright wrote on their experiments,* it did two things: (a) measured the electrical charge in the air by introducing its own charge and seeing how long it took to cancel out, and (b) ascertained atmospheric radiation by introducing a mildly radioactive element to the environment, which would react with radiation in the air and produce a quantifiable charge. As Wright was studying radiation and Simpson was a leading meteorologist – a field which was, at the time, questioning whether atmospheric charge had any effect on weather – these experiments were in both their interests.

The electroscope used on the *Terra Nova* is on display at the Polar Museum in Cambridge, so that much – the boxy piece on top – is accurate. The rest of the device is based on a photo of something similar from a 1910 article in *Scientific American*, with help from an unexpected source: a prank recorded in Cherry's diary, wherein other members of the crew rigged up a mock device to spoof the scientists. There was an antenna (made from a walking stick with a cork wired to it) and the electroscope (two ginger beer bottles); there was also a timer (an alarm clock wound and rung every minute) and something that hummed (Tryggve Gran). The machine described in Simpson and Wright's paper had, for its antenna, a short copper rod coated with ionium and soldered with sulphur to a metre-long wooden rod – not unlike a walking stick – and the one photographed in *Scientific American* has a bell on the left side of the base and possibly a dynamo on the right, which would have hummed.

In order to get a proper run of readings, the machine needed to be operated at regular intervals over a 24-hour span, but it was very difficult to get a full 24 hours in which environmental factors remained constant – changes in cloud cover and wind direction could influence the readings, and even a resetting of sail could be disruptive. Simpson and Wright's paper presents what observations they did make, but bemoans the difficulty of getting a sufficient number of scientifically valid data sets, and admits the likelihood that, in consequence, their findings may be shaky. However, this line of inquiry had mostly been conducted over land, and most other ships of the time had metal hulls, which could interfere with electromagnetic fields, so readings collected on a wooden ship crossing half the world's oceans were still of interest, even if they weren't perfect. When they arrived in New Zealand, they submitted their heavily-proviso'd paper, and it was published while they were in Antarctica.

*Simpson, G. C., and C. S. Wright. "Atmospheric Electricity over the Ocean." *Proceedings of the Royal Society of London.* Series A, Containing Papers of a Mathematical and Physical Character 85, no. 577 (1911): 175-99.

2. WJ 2 The quote in the following panel is also from p.2 but paraphrased.

3. WJ 2, ed.

4. They started seeing flying fish after leaving Madeira – same for the man-o-war on the next page – so this is a bit premature, but they were nice bits of fun to use for the introductions.

5. WJ 4 – Wright's bit is paraphrased.

6. WJ 2, ed. – Oates was counted as part of the scientific staff for administrative purposes, but was not a scientist.

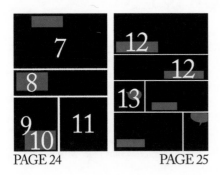

PAGE 24   PAGE 25

7. Nelson caught a man-o-war (*Physalia physalis*) on 6 July 1910 and everyone enjoyed admiring it, while it "vigorously tried to sting all who touched it." [WJ 7] Despite its appearance, this creature is not in fact a jellyfish, nor indeed even one creature. Rather, it is a symbiotic colony of specialised but genetically identical individuals suspended beneath an air bladder, the sail of which catches the wind and pulls them around the surface of the ocean. Their stings are powerful enough to kill a fish (the colony's food) and can cause a human severe pain and symptoms resembling anaphylactic shock. The sting is rarely fatal in itself, but people have died trying to swim back to shore while in distress. And if that wasn't metal enough, the air bladder is filled mainly with carbon monoxide. Best avoided. Do not poke.

8. WJ 4

9. The instrument Pennell is using here is a Lloyd Creak Dip Circle, which measures the angle of the Earth's magnetic field and its strength. Just as a compass, held flat, aligns with the magnetic field to show you north, turning the compass on its side will show you the orientation of the field vertically. At the equator, the needle will rest parallel to the horizon, but the further you are towards a pole, the more it dips to follow the field running into the centre of the Earth.

The extreme downward angle of the magnetic field in polar regions makes using regular compasses difficult, as the needle wants to dig into the face of the compass rather than swing about in a helpful way. This can be compensated for by adding a small weight to the opposite end of the needle, but one still has to stand perfectly still for several very cold minutes waiting for the needle to calm down and find north when all the forces are saying "down."

The compass needle aligns with the Earth's magnetic field.

Near the magnetic pole, the magnetic field intersects with the Earth's surface, and pulls the needle down. The degree of 'dip' indicates how close you are to the magnetic pole.

Further from the pole, the magnetic field is roughly parallel to the Earth's surface, so the needle is level with the horizon.

If you know where the magnetic poles are, the amount of dip can tell you your latitude, but unlike the geographical poles, the magnetic poles wander around over time. Knowing the precise location of the north and south magnetic poles is very important to an empire which rules the waves, and the Royal Navy was invested in acquiring superior knowledge of the science behind their navigational instruments. Mapping the magnetic poles, and local variations in the magnetic field, was at least as important as mapping the world geographically, and Pennell was contributing to this.

10. WJ 4, ed.

11. One regular job was moving tons of coal from the *Terra Nova*'s cargo hold into the bunkers, from which it could be fed to the boiler. This was called "trimming", and was a dirty and arduous job. "There wasn't an officer on the ship who did not shift coal till he was sick of the sight of it, but

I heard no complaints." [WJ 2; the narration here is edited from the same page] They may not have complained out loud, but one hears a lot about trimming coal in their diaries.

12. WJ 3, ed.

13. Frederick Hooper – who you saw serving tea on the bridge at the beginning of this sequence – was the steward, whose responsibilities included waking everyone up. He doesn't get a special intro because you don't really need to know who he is until they get to Antarctica. But now you do. Cherry sometimes gets called the youngest member of the expedition, but in fact that was Hooper.

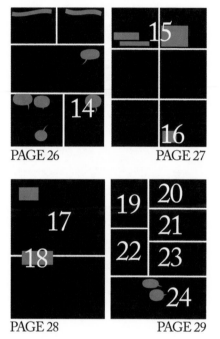

PAGE 26   PAGE 27

PAGE 28   PAGE 29

14. "A first-rate craft and sails like a witch in spite of her lumping bulk." (From a letter to his mother, quoted in Seaver's *Bowers*, p.151) Bowers' opinion of the *Terra Nova* was a lot rosier than anyone else's, perhaps because he was enjoying being back on a sailing ship after a few years under steam.

15. The text in these two panels is cobbled together from lines on WJ 4 and 5.

16. WJ 4

17. I've put many miles into the research of this book, but relative to its narrative importance, a trip to Madeira was beyond what time and budget allowed. This episode owes much to Google Image Search, which was very helpful in terms of the island itself but not so much for views of it from the sea. I have made up something here which, I hope, looks nice, and like it could be Madeira. Similarly, there may be no quay in Funchal harbour which has a view of the city like this, but it got a lot of storytelling done in one panel. If someone would like to put me on a boat to Madeira I will happily redraw both this and the two long-distance views.

18. WJ 3 up to "required", the rest by me.

19. "Gran had been to the top of the island with a Portuguese to photograph him at the top. We never understood why he took with him a large rucksack containing his Norwegian naval uniform and a hammock and a Japanese umbrella made of paper. Apparently he reached the top naked, having dropped his clothes one by one on account of the heat." [EAW, 24-25 June 1910] According to Cherry's diary, a funicular railway went most of the way up, then Gran hiked the rest. I don't know which peak it was that he climbed, but Pico Arieiro turned up in a lot of tourism material, so that's what I've used.

20. Bowers kept up a regular and voluminous correspondence with his mother and sisters. I may have overstated quite how much mail he would have picked up in Madeira, only ten days out, but this is the impression one gets of his mailbag from the archives. He's in his "whites" here as they were in his wardrobe on the outward journey, and would have been more dressy for going ashore. The fruit tree here is a loquat – both Cherry and Wilson mention their abundance, and Cherry ate "loquats galore". They have fuzzy skin, like an apricot but more leathery, and taste like a ripe pear crossed with a tart nectarine.

21. Cherry wrote that he went for lunch and then had a bath; both were good, but the bath was better. He also took the time to document his bath on arriving in Cape Town, and mentions baths or lack thereof a few times on the journey. I can only surmise he was a man who loved his baths.

22. Wilson's diary implies that everyone ran off to the tourist attractions of Madeira, as he had done when he came through on the Discovery Expedition in 1901. The list of these includes "toboggan rides down the cobbled streets". To my great surprise, tobogganing down the streets of Madeira is still a thing you can do! Nowadays, though, there are more parked cars and fewer cobbles.

23. Wilson forfeited Madeira's amusements to work on illustrations for an official report on a disease which had been killing grouse in Scotland. This investigation had taken up most of his years between coming off the *Discovery* and setting out on the *Terra Nova*, work which involved tramping over miles of moorland and dissecting hundreds of grouse. He was still trying to finish the illustrations on the *Terra Nova*, often waking well before dawn to get some painting in before the ship's workday properly started. Madeira offered a useful chunk of free time, and he made the most of it – "From Friday breakfast time to Sunday breakfast time I had something like 7 hours sleep, and I fear some of the 25 letters written from here will have read like it too, for I was latterly quite unable to keep awake for more than a line or two at a time." [EAW 24-25 June 1910] He actually did this work in a room inside the café, but both Wilson and I can look forward to many panels depicting him painting indoors, so I let him have a nice sunny terrace for once.

24. Cherry, Gran, and a few others had dinner on the evening after Gran's mountaineering adventure, whereupon Cherry recorded this excellent line of dialogue. Gran hadn't eaten all day, apparently. [ACG 24 June 1910]

They are eating at the terrace restaurant of Reid's Palace, which is actually where Cherry had lunch; the dinner was at Central. Reid's had been the epicentre of a typhoid outbreak not long before the *Terra Nova* arrived. Madeira's water was deemed safe to drink by then, but they decided

not to fill the *Terra Nova*'s tanks with it just in case, which is why they were so short of water through the doldrums. [EAW 24-25 June 1910] I had wanted to include this fact as a *memento mori* – a reminder of death even in the midst of abundant life and colour – but I couldn't find a way to do it gracefully and keep the episode short, so it's relegated to the annotations. RIP, factoid.

25. WS:TSL 34 – As with most information poured from Taylor's pen, the account of swinging ship which I have used for reference here is but one leaf in an information salad, so is perhaps not as thoroughly explanatory as it might be. If I have got it wrong, I sincerely apologise.

PAGE 30

THE DOLDRUMS

1. Cherry gives the sound of the engine room as a *chonk chonk chonk* so loud one had to shout to be heard. Unfortunately, "chonk" currently means "fat, in a cute way" in Internet slang. The Internet is ephemeral, and *Worst Journey* has lasted a hundred years, so I hope that sticking with the original is worthwhile.

2. "Four hours in the boiling fiery furnace which the Terra Nova's stokehold formed in the tropics ... was a real test of staying power ..." [WJ 9] After a day or two of people getting heat exhaustion, they went down to two-hour shifts. The boiler was constantly going, to power the ship through the doldrums, so the temperature in the hold rose until, by 10 July, it was 105°F (40.5°C). [EAW 10 July 1910] Officers would not normally have been feeding the furnaces, but one of the stokers was off sick, so they filled in for a time. [EAW 8 July 1910]

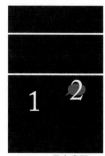

PAGE 31

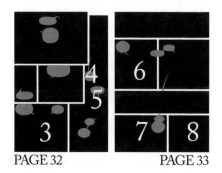

PAGE 32   PAGE 33

3. This implement is called the "devil" and was used to rake the hot coals into the best shape for heating the boiler, and to break up the clinker. "[T]he actual shovelling of the coal into the furnaces, one after the other, was as child's play to handling the 'devil'". [WJ 9]

4. Silas read Dante's *Inferno* on the journey to the Pole, but it seemed a fitting reference in the engine room.

5. Bowers really was this cheerful.

6. "But inasmuch as some of the officers were coaling almost daily, they found that any amount of cold sea water, even with a euphemistically named 'sea-water soap,' had no very great effect in removing the coal dust. The alternative was to make friends with the engine-room authorities and draw some water from the boilers." [WJ 8]

7. Nelson got the nickname "Marie" for wearing an "immaculate" collar for dinner. I've gathered that this was a topical reference, after a Marie Ducas or Ducart, but I haven't found who she was, or why a sharp dresser (or a fallen one) should be named after her. (See p.175, note 25.)

8. WJ 7

9. "... [A] complete hourly log was kept ... of the numbers and species which were seen .... Though many helped, this log was largely the work of Pennell, who was an untiring and exact observer." [WJ 8] I've tried to make a running gag out of Pennell suddenly appearing whenever anything needs doing, because that's the impression one gets of him from the diaries. I'm not sure it happens often enough for anyone to notice, but now you know and can watch out for it.

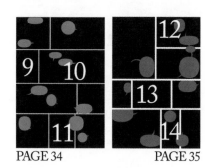

PAGE 34   PAGE 35

10.   Lillie, the other marine biologist, who was most especially interested in whales and dolphins, caught measles in Cardiff or Madeira. They turned the as-yet-unoccupied photographic darkroom into a sickbay and kept him quarantined there. [EAW 1 July 1910]

11.   It was Nelson, not Pennell, who gave Cherry a navigation lesson [ACG 3 July 1910]. I have given this job to Pennell because, first, he was the navigator; second, we will be seeing a lot more of Nelson later and I want to feature Pennell as much as I can while we're still with the ship. He gets written out of a lot of Expedition histories because he wasn't in Antarctica with the main party, but he was a much-loved and important member of the Expedition, so deserves some time in the spotlight. I'm certain he would have been a much better teacher than I have written him to be, but it's important that Cherry struggle with navigation for story reasons, and that you sympathise with his struggle, so I had to make it sound confusing.

Cherry's navigation lesson was actually on the evening of 1 July, and his Havana dream immediately followed it. Wilson and Cherry did their turn in the stokehold on 8 July, so I have set everything on that date.

12.   Cherry was bad at maths, and the resulting anxiety around the subject probably didn't help.

13.   The ship's bell was the means of keeping time, and thus work shifts – or "watches" as they are called on a ship. All personnel are assigned to a watch, which is on duty four hours a day. The bell would be rung once for every elapsed half hour, so ringing four sets of two ("eight bells") signified the end of a watch. This is why, a few minutes later, it's bath time for the stokers.

The bell of the *Terra Nova* now lives at the Scott Polar Research Institute, and is rung for tea at five bells forenoon (10:30am) and eight bells afternoon (4:00pm). I have not been able to find where it was on the ship, but it was probably on the bridge somewhere, because it would be rung by an officer of the watch. The few photos I've found of the bridge only show the telegraph to the engine room, which was on the starboard side of the chart house, so I put the bell to port.

14.   These are pages from *Hints to Travellers*, a navigational companion book from the 1890s which they had on the Expedition. Celestial navigation involves a little bit of looking at stars and a lot of looking up numbers in eye-crossing tables. I have been deliberately confusing on this page, but if you want to have a go at understanding it properly, I can recommend Abrian Curington's Star Math series: https://bluecatco.com/star-math/

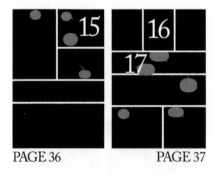

PAGE 36   PAGE 37

15.   Bowers loved to swim, and wasn't shy about getting his kit off. When Debenham (who we will meet later) reminisced about joining the *Terra Nova*, he described finding Bowers in the wardroom having a bath, and made it sound like he jumped out of it to take the new recruits up the mainmast in the nude – perhaps not what Deb meant to imply, but after you've read a fair bit about Bowers, it's entirely plausible. If you can find the 1966 *Reader's Digest* volume which contains a condensed version of *Scott's Last Expedition*, Debenham tells the story in there.

16.   I don't know what Cherry's optical prescription was, but he described people walking on the other side of the street as "blobs". [Wheeler, 60] Scott wrote: "Cherry-Garrard is remarkable because of his eyes. He can only see through glasses and has to wrestle with all sorts of inconveniences in consequence. Yet one could never guess it – for he manages somehow to do more than his share of the work." [RFS 13 Feb 1911]

17.   EAW 9 July 1910

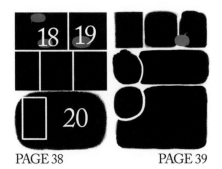

PAGE 38   PAGE 39

18. Silas described the Nursery in just these terms in his diary. [CSW, 15 July 1910] One door of the Nursery let onto the boiler room, and with the tropical humidity it was something of a sauna.

19. Silas was a notorious pottymouth, and seemed (in writing, at least) to express himself more fluently in mathematical equations than English. To keep this book family-friendly but still in character, I'm censoring him with equations instead of the more traditional string of typographical symbols. This, here, is an equation for radioactive decay.

20. This was apparently the first instance of what would become a recurring dream, which he first recorded in his diary on 1 July 1910 and then recalled in his foreword to George Seaver's biography of Wilson in 1933 [Seaver's *Wilson*, xi]. In this dream, he finds that he's navigating a ship out of Havana Harbour and he has gone to sleep without laying her course. He wakes (within the dream) to find the ship running onto the headland, and tries to wake Bill to ask what he ought to do. In 1910, real-life Bill tried to insist he needn't do anything; in 1933, the whole episode is a dream.

The choice of Havana harbour had always puzzled me – I knew Cherry had done a bit of travelling before the expedition, but I didn't think he'd been to Cuba. Then, visiting the *Terra Nova* collection at the Canterbury Museum in Christchurch, I saw the cigar box pictured here, and it all fell into place.

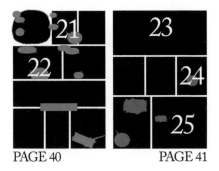

PAGE 40   PAGE 41

21. Cherry was a regular sleepwalker and sleep talker, which his companions took in good fun, but he found it rather embarrassing.

22. Bill did make a point to sketch the sunrises any day there was one.

23. This section is mostly a fabrication, based very loosely on the events of 12 July 1910 [WJ 9] to stand in for the "learning to sail" moments that would have happened piecemeal through the early part of the journey. In place of citations of this bit, then, here is some general sailing information which I hope will elucidate the process for you ...

165

Setting and furling sail follows a series of steps. They are setting sail in this sequence, but I find that it's easier to understand the logic of the process by describing how sail is furled:

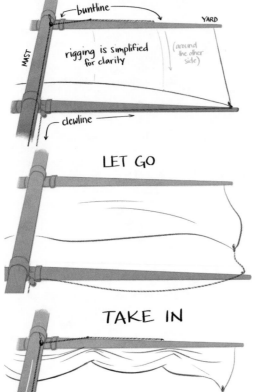

When in use, the sail is held taut between the **yard** – the horizontal wooden thing that the top of the sail is attached to – and its lower corners, or **clews**, which attach the sail either to the ship itself, or to the yard of the sail below it.

To **let it go,** first you relax the sail by releasing the **clewline**, which holds the clews tight to the lower yard.

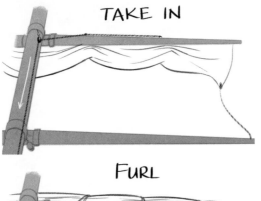

Then you **take it in** by pulling on the **buntlines**, which act like the drawstring on window blinds, pulling the sail up to the yard.

Only then do you climb up the mast to **furl** it, which means piling it all on top of the yard and tying it down. If you expect to be needing it again soon, you don't furl it, you just leave it taken in – that keeps it on standby, so you can set it again quickly when you need to, just by pulling ropes on deck.

So, what you see on these pages, when they're setting sail, is the reverse: First, men go aloft (up amongst the sails and rigging) to untie the furled sail from the top of the yard, and let it fall. Now, at Campbell's order, the men on deck will haul the clewline to pull the corners of the sail tight to the yard below, so it can catch the wind. You generally have a lot more men on deck pulling on ropes than men aloft. Given the attention paid to going aloft in movies, it's surprising just how much sail management is done by pulling ropes on deck, but it's much faster and safer that way.

24. Davies informs us that nearly all rope work on a sailing ship is done to the accompaniment of a shanty [Francis Davies, *With Scott Before The Mast*, p.38], and there will be plenty of shanties to come. When I went on the SV *Tenacious* to research this book, we heaved not to a shanty but to this "two six" chant. I don't know if it's standard, but in the limited space of a comic, it evokes the rhythm of hauling better than the many words of a song. Including this chant is my little tribute to the Jubilee Sailing Trust; without my week with them, this book would be much less authentic.

25. The thrilling image of a tall ship with all her sails billowing isn't usually what they look like. A strategic selection of sails tends to be the norm; which ones are set depends on wind strength and direction. For the most part I've tried to draw the *Terra Nova* with the sails as they were set at the time, if it was recorded. Cherry did say they set all sail here, though, and I am not one to pass up an exciting visual when it's offered to me.

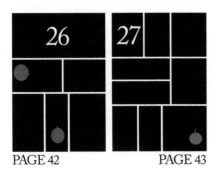

PAGE 42   PAGE 43

26. Tropical rain showers meant refilling the drinking water and being able to do one's laundry. [WJ 9] Unfortunately, no amount of caulking stopped the water streaming into their bunks, and with the heat, this made the interior of the ship rather steamy.

27. The rope strung along underneath the yard, on which one stands while handling the sail, is called the *jumpline*. It is named such because when you're standing on it, and someone else gets on it, the leverage of their weight sends you a foot or more upwards. Exciting!

CROSSING THE LINE

I devised this sequence with the help of a few journals and a commemorative booklet for the H.M.S. *Renown*'s Crossing the Line ceremony in 1920, which resembled the *Terra Nova*'s very closely. In the year between drawing and colouring this sequence, the journal of Francis Davies, carpenter on the *Terra Nova*, was published. I discovered that he had by far the most detailed description of the costumes and rites, and that most of what I'd drawn was wrong. But it was too late to change everything. If you would like to get the facts, and a great many amusing anecdotes besides, please check out *With Scott Before The Mast* (Reardon Publishing, 2020).

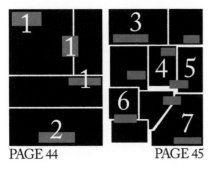

PAGE 44   PAGE 45

1. WJ 10, edited and expanded for clarification.

2. The token of the Order was something like a sea serpent crossed with a dragon, according to Wright. It had been made by the ship's carpenter and painted in rainbow colours by Wilson. [CSW 15 July 1910]

3. According to Wilson there were ten inductees, both officers and seamen. Cherry was not among them because he'd travelled to Australia already. [Wheeler, 55] I've chosen a smaller group for simplicity's sake. In the same interest of economy

I've made Oates and Atkinson the only Bears when in fact there were four, and have left out some of Neptune's retinue.

4. I have also economised some of the ceremony, otherwise we'd be here all day. It started with the Doctor taking the patient's temperature; Wright records that the doctor read his temperature as -70°F and said he was quite ill. No matter the ailment, the treatment was always a pill and a drink; the drink was vinegar and cayenne pepper, and the pill was an egg-sized ball of flour and fat that may also have included soap and more cayenne. [CSW, EAW]

5. The initiate was lathered from the top of his head to his waist in a paste of flour and soot. [CSW]

6. Wright says the razor was two feet long, Wilson three; I have gone for comically oversized but not too awkward for staging purposes.

7. "Nelson created a diversion by taking the Barber into the bath with him quite unexpectedly." [EAW 15 July 1910]

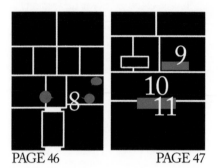

PAGE 46   PAGE 47

8. The scenario with Gran is related in *Worst Journey*, p.10.

9. WJ 10

10. Tryggve Gran's recollection of the Expedition is notoriously unreliable, and often easily refutable, so it's wise to take what he says with a grain of salt, especially later in life. One of these later statements* tells an intriguing story about Dennis Lillie: During the celebrations after Crossing the Line, Gran says, Lillie confided to him that he believed himself to be a woman in a man's body, and that he blushed at the sight of naked men. Now, it's not a given that Gran remembered this correctly so many years later, or that he hadn't misunderstood at the time. Gender and sexual boundaries were drawn differently back then, and hardly mentioned; it's difficult to know how, or if, anyone would fit the labels we use today. However, Lillie did have a nervous breakdown after the First World War, and lived out his latter days in an asylum, which is not incompatible with the treatment of transgender people in those days. His medical records won't be available until 2063, so we have to wait until then to know. I have Lillie blushing here anyway; the reader can decide whether it's from pride, embarrassment, excess scrubbing, or something else.

*Gran, letter to G. Hutchinson, c. 1968, quoted in Wheeler, 197; see also https://museumofthemind.org.uk/blog/in-the-spotlight-dennis-lillie

11. WJ 10

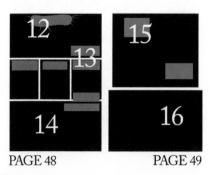

PAGE 48   PAGE 49

12. Cherry says this song was "conspicuous" in the expedition's repertoire around this time. It was implied to refer to Campbell, "who was the only father on board and whose hair was popularly supposed to be getting thinner" though he was "always at work" so it must have been sung with tongue in cheek. [WJ 11]

13. The narration on this page is drawn from *Worst Journey* pp.10-11, with some minor edits.

168

14. I have combined two truths to tell an untruth here, in this panel. They are:

a. To celebrate a man's birthday, he was passed bodily over the beam which bisected the skylight in the wardroom. [WS:TSL 73]

b. Wilson's birthday was 23 July, which did fall between crossing the Equator and arriving at South Trinidad. However, Wilson's birthday was overlooked – it was only remembered just before midnight by Bowers, who kicked off a clamour in order to rouse everyone to celebrate. [EAW 24 July 1910]

The game named by Cherry as making people laugh till they cried – "The Priest of the Parish Has Lost His Cap" – is a verbal game, so difficult to illustrate. Wilson's next birthday is going to be spent in a hurricane-force blizzard at Cape Crozier. I've bent history a little for the sake of visual storytelling, and this delectable contrast.

15. The narration on this page is gleaned from pp.11-12 of *Worst Journey*.

16. This view of South Trinidad is taken directly from a picture Wilson painted when they stopped here on the *Discovery* in 1901.

SOUTH TRINIDAD

The island known in 1910 as South Trinidad is now officially Brazilian territory, and called Ilha Trinidade. I have once again played with time here: In actual fact, the *Terra Nova* dropped anchor the night of 25 July, they explored the island on the 26th, and sailed away the morning of the 27th. I have made it all happen in one day, as that makes more intuitive sense to the reader.

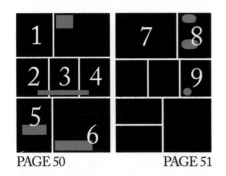

PAGE 50   PAGE 51

1. The *Terra Nova* anchored in West Bay, "and the sea was so clear we could see the anchor at the bottom in 15 fathoms. A number of sharks and other fish appeared at once …" [Bowers, WJ 16]

2. The expedition had no botanist – there wasn't need for one in Antarctica – and their geologists would be joining them in Australia. Lillie, marine biologist, took on the botany and geology jobs here. [WJ 17]

3. Nelson and Simpson trekked "along the shore for sea beasts". [Bowers, WJ 17]

4. Bowers was a keen butterfly collector and didn't mind insects generally, but had an intense fear of spiders, a running peril during his service in the Tropics – being surprised by one in his cabin once, he wrote home, "If it was a Cobra I should have been cool but a spider!!!" [Anne Strathie, *Birdie Bowers: Captain Scott's Marvel*, p.40] Of South Trinidad, he wrote "others helped me catch them, of course" [WJ 18] – in this case Wright, a fellow arachnophobe [CSW 14].

5. The sick sailor was named Brewster, and he was was the main reason the *Terra Nova* didn't leave until the 27th – the sea was too high to get him safely off on the 26th.

6. "We found lots of little tern and terns' eggs, lying on the bare rock with no nest at all." [WJ 14] The British Museum mentioned here is what we now know as the Natural History Museum, which was, institutionally, part of the British Museum at the time. The skins collected on South Trinidad are still in the Natural History Museum's collection at Tring.

7. The raised beach visible here factored into one of Lillie's "many ingenious theories" about the island, to explain all the dead trees, which had no living counterparts. Lillie thought the island must have risen at some point recently, and the change in elevation and/or climate caused these trees to die and tumble down the slopes. [SWS 31]

8. The petrel nesting site here is based on a photograph from the Discovery Expedition. "This bird [the Trinidad Petrel] has been given no less than three specific names but I am sure they all interbreed and are really the same species. Besides being called *Oestrelata trinitatis* it is also called *Oe. arminjoniana* and *Oe. wilsoni* after me – but we found every phase together nesting along cliff edges, dark and pale – young and old." [EAW, 26 July 1910] The species have, in fact, since been proven to be one, and have been reclassified as *Pterodroma arminjoniana*. The chick as I have drawn it is younger than they found them; many had already fledged.

9. It was the terns that would land on people's heads, but I have folded that fact into the petrel episode for narrative expediency. As with many places free of mammalian predators, the birds on South Trinidad had little or no fear of humans.

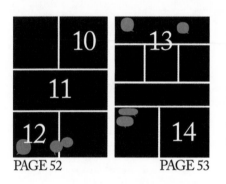

PAGE 52   PAGE 53

10. "These crabs were round us in thousands – I counted seven watching me out of one crack between two rocks." [WJ 14]

11. The birding party had their lunch somewhere short of the summit and then climbed all the way to the top. I've collapsed these two stops into one.

The bushes had acrid berries which the crabs would climb up and eat, but they would also lie about sunning themselves on the tops of the foliage. [WJ 14]

12. WJ 14

13. "The crabs gathered round us in a circle, with their eyes turning towards us – as if they were waiting for us to die to come and eat us. One big fellow left his place in the circle and waddled up to my feet and examined my boots. First with one claw and then with the other he took a taste of my boot. He went away obviously disgusted: one could almost see him shake his head." [WJ 14]

I had thought Cherry was excessively anthropomorphising here, but it's very easy to do that with these crabs, which resemble some sort of Pokemon. Look up the Ascension land crab (*Johngarthia lagostoma*) and see.

14. "We had a big and fast scramble down …" [WJ 15]

15. In truth, both Cherry's and Wilson's guns were badly dented [EAW, 26 July 1910], but Cherry falling and breaking things comes up again later, so I've employed a bit of foreshadowing here at his expense.

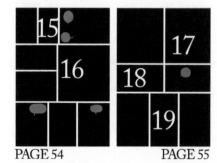

PAGE 54   PAGE 55

16. Most of the action on this page is taken from WJ 15.

17. I've left out how Hooper (foreground in this panel) almost died on his way out to the boats, which you can find both in *Worst Journey* [WJ 15] and Wilson's diary [26 July 1910]. He got the worst of an incoming wave, and though miraculously not pulped on the rocks, he lost grip of the rope and was underwater long enough that they expected he'd drowned. "[Wilson] remarked afterwards to me ... that it was a curious thing that a number of men, knowing that there was nothing they could do, could quietly watch a man fighting for his life, and he did not think that any but the British temperament could do so." [WJ 16]

18. "When we first got down to the shore and things were looking nasty, Wilson sat down on the top of a rock and ate a biscuit in the coolest possible manner. It was an example to avoid all panicking ..." [WJ 15-16]

19. You can find the details of this exciting moment in Bowers' journal, quoted in WJ 19-20.

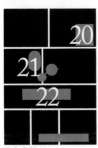

PAGE 56

20. WJ 21, ed.

21. Cobbled together from references on WJ 16.

22. WJ 22, ed.

These pages are true to the spirit of getting off South Trinidad, and not exactly false in the particulars, but I give you entirely the wrong impression of time and, if anything, dramatically understate the size of the waves.

It was a race to get off the island between the recall signal at 4 P.M. and sunset at 6. Because of the high surf they could not bring the boats close to shore, so everyone swam out along a rope, as I've drawn it. This meant they had to leave their specimens and gear behind for the night – along with Brewster and Atkinson – and return in the morning to get it off. It was much simpler, narratively, to make this all happen in one go, but it meant mashing both days into one. My greatest regret is not getting to draw Atkinson and Brewster on a sea cliff being menaced by crabs and terns all night, shivering around one box of matches. Perhaps I will draw this for my own pleasure one day.

As for the surf, there is a picture in Atkinson's scrapbook which shows just how high the waves crashed. Cherry says they were 30 feet above the water when they first got soaked, and the waves in the photo are easily that high or more. I could say that I toned it down because I want to save the real drama for the big storm later, but really it's because I couldn't figure out how to give the appropriate scale to the waves *and* show what people were doing in the same panel. Cutting wide and close again would have made this section too long. I hope it still comes across as dramatic, but it's far less dramatic than it actually was.

SOUTH ATLANTIC

These pages are a direct visual translation of the opening of Chapter 2 in *Worst Journey*.

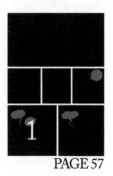

1. The phrase "two hoops" was used in the Antarctic to describe severe weather, usually a blizzard. I've not seen it in anyone's diaries before then, but Cherry wrote it into *Worst Journey* here, and he's the boss. [WJ 24] In the book it's an anonymous seaman who wakes him up, but Silas was on the watch before Cherry's and I thought it better to have a familiar face.

2. Water leaked through the deck which formed the ceiling of the Nursery, so the inhabitants of the upper bunks constructed a series of chutes to divert it away from their mattresses.

PAGE 57

3. The instrument which Cherry checks here should be a barograph, a device with a rotating drum of paper on which a lever records atmospheric pressure over time. A barometer is a clearer visual, though. This particular barometer has been nicked from the wardroom of the *Discovery*.

PAGE 58   PAGE 59

4. Cherry took over as Campbell's midshipman from Gran, who was unhappy about being treated like a servant, or "domestic." Gran's English not yet being perfect, what Gran had actually complained of was being treated as a "drumstick." [WJ 26]

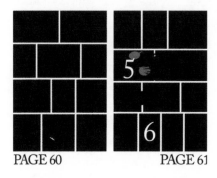

5. Pennell officially shared a cabin with Campbell, but preferred to sleep under the chart table, no matter the weather.

6. I have changed the commands from what's in the book, because it's much easier for a static drawing to show a sail being let go than a yard being lowered. [WJ 27]

PAGE 60   PAGE 61

7. Hooper – who, as steward was responsible for getting everyone out of bed – was the tallest man on the expedition, and Bowers was the shortest.

8. "One of the most popular [shanties] describes the adventures of a mythical hero, 'Ranzo' who 'was no sailor' at the beginning of the epic, but being taught navigation by an unusually affable captain,*

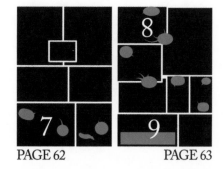

PAGE 62   PAGE 63

ends up by realizing that proud position himself! The chorus, 'Ranzo, boys, Ranzo,' is easily remembered." [WS:TSL, 48-49]

*This is not exactly how the shanty goes, but I leave you the pleasure of looking it up.

9. I have compressed two paragraphs into a few lines. The full background to the pumps is thus:

> From first to last these pumps were a source of much exercise and hearty curses. A wooden ship always leaks a little, but the amount of water taken in by the Terra Nova even in calm weather was extraordinary, and could not be traced until the ship was dry-docked in Lyttelton, New Zealand, and the forepart was flooded.
>
> In the meantime the ship had to be kept as dry as possible, a process which was not facilitated by forty gallons of oil which got loose during the rough weather after leaving South Trinidad, and found its way into the bilges. As we found later, some never-to-be-sufficiently-cursed stevedore had left one of the bottom boards only half-fitted into its neighbours. In consequence the coal dust and small pieces of coal, which was stowed in this hold, found their way into the bilges. Forty gallons of oil completed the havoc and the pumps would gradually get more and more blocked until it was necessary to send for Davies, the carpenter, to take parts of them to pieces and clear out the oily coal balls which had stopped them. This pumping would sometimes take till nearly eight, and then would always have to be repeated again in the evening, and sometimes every watch had to take a turn. At any rate it was good for our muscles. [WJ 28]

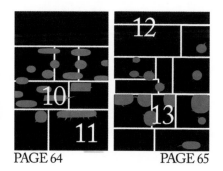

PAGE 64   PAGE 65

10. Having just come off his watch, Cherry is making up the ship's log. "... force of the wind, state of the sea, height of the barometer, and all the details which a log has to carry—including a reading of the distance run as shown by the patent log line—(many is the time I have forgotten to take it just at the hour and have put down what I thought it ought to be, and not what it was)." [WJ 30]

11. Wait, what on earth just happened?! I can hear your bafflement through time and space. Here is Cherry's explanation for this nautical antiphon:

> Pennell is the navigator, and the standard compass, owing to its remoteness from iron in this position, is placed on the top of the ice-house. The steersman, however, steers by a binnacle compass placed aft in front of his wheel. But these two compasses for various reasons do not read alike at a given moment, while the standard is the truer of the two.
>
> At intervals, then, Pennell or the officer of the watch orders the steersman to "Stand by for a steady," and goes up to the standard compass, and watches the needle. Suppose the course laid down is S. 40 E. A liner would steer almost true to this course unless there was a big wind or sea. But not so the old Terra Nova. Even with a good steersman the needle swings a good many degrees either side of the S. 40 E. But as it steadies momentarily on the exact course Pennell shouts his "Steady," the steersman reads just where the needle is pointing on the compass card before him, say S. 47 E., and knows that this is the course which is to be steered by the binnacle compass.
>
> Pennell's yells were so frequent and ear-piercing that he became famous for them, and many times in working on the ropes in rough seas and big winds, we have been cheered by this unmusical noise over our heads. [WJ 30]

12. This page is inspired by Cherry's and Wilson's diaries for 1 Aug 1910. Other sources say albatrosses were caught by trapping their beaks in a triangular piece of metal, but the bent nail trick, which was used for smaller seabirds, is a lot easier to communicate.

13. Both Wilson and Cherry would get the worse end of an albatross' bill before the journey was done, but not today!

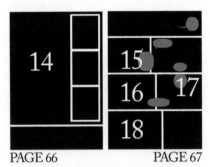

PAGE 66   PAGE 67

14. This cross-section of the *Terra Nova* was cobbled together from a number of different sources:
• the ship's plans (which are rather taciturn when it comes to the specifics of the engineering)
• a cutaway illustration, possibly from the *Illustrated London News*
• the tiny model engine in the cutaway *Discovery* model at Discovery Point
• the engine room of the *Berkeley*, a former Sausalito ferry, now at the San Diego Maritime Museum.

15. Between the Discovery and Terra Nova expeditions, Wilson was commissioned to investigate a disease killing off grouse in Scotland. It entailed many years trekking over rainy moors and dissecting hundreds of birds, and having two years' worth of notes stolen in Glasgow. [Seaver's *Wilson*, 161] When Scott offered him the post of Head of Scientific Staff on the Terra Nova Expedition, Wilson thought he would have the Grouse Report done and dusted, but he was still working on illustrations during the first leg of the trip.

16. Wilson developed this practice of noting the colours on a pencil sketch when he was attempting to recuperate from tuberculosis in Norway (a sojourn which involved a lot more hiking than recuperation, but that's another story).

17. He's right, you know.

18. "Had a splendid view of the green flash at sunset which appeared about 15 seconds after the sun had been covered by a large distant swell on the horizon. We expected to see the sun again but saw the green flash instead – most distinctly." [EAW, 10 Aug 1910]
    The green flash is an illusion caused by the refraction of light through layers in the Earth's atmosphere when the sun is at or just under the horizon. Originally I had just the flash and not the sun, as Wilson described, but this confused people, and adding the sun back in seemed to help. I had assumed that once an atmospheric phenomenon is a plot point in a major Hollywood blockbuster (in this case, *Pirates of the Caribbean: At World's End*) it would be common knowledge, but it seems not.

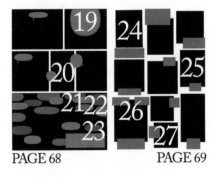

PAGE 68   PAGE 69

19. Yes, this was actually their grace before meals. It's mentioned in a few accounts, but the most complete lyrics are found in Katherine Lambert's *Hell With A Capital H* (p.64). Despite its popularity on the expedition, this music hall song has not survived long enough to get onto the Internet in any form that I've been able to find. More's the pity.

20. The ship's cat lived with the seamen in the fo'c'sle, and while he may have been welcome in the wardroom there is no record of a visit. I invented this scene so I could share one of my favourite anecdotes about Bowers:

> Now he hated spiders but he loved cats, and when eight years old was found sleeping on the floor rather than disturb the cat which occupied the middle of his bed. Sometimes he stood beside his chair during a meal because the cat had got there first; nobody thought it strange; nobody offered him another seat; it seemed quite natural to them, and his mother, being fond of cats herself, took no notice. [Cherry-Garrard, foreword to Seaver's *Bowers*, xv]

The cat, by the way, has a very rude name, which was sadly common for pets at the time. I have no reason to include it, and doing so would create an enormous distraction from the actual story, so I have left it out. Consider this your warning, should you pick up the original book.

21. The S.S. *Waratah* was the MH370 of the day – a passenger steamer which had disappeared somewhere on its way to Cape Town, with no trace ever found. It's believed that there was a boiler explosion. When the *Terra Nova* arrived at South Trinidad, the planet Venus happened to be aligned with a mountain peak, and for a moment Wilson and Campbell wondered if it were a beacon fire lit by survivors of the *Waratah* who might have washed up there. [EAW 26 July 1910]

22. "One does pall of champagne, beer and ginger ale in the course of time. Indeed I can think of nothing more calculated to turn a man a rabid T.T. [teetotaller] than a voyage on the *Terra Nova*, R.Y.S." [CSW, 10 July 1910]

23. Simpson was from Manchester, and came from a more working-class background than many of the other scientists. He was a bit of a socialist, and keen to argue about any subject, political or otherwise, that offered itself. [CSW 2 Oct 1910]

24. This picture of Scott is a portrait painted after the Discovery Expedition, which now hangs at the National Portrait Gallery in London.

25. Nelson was first called "The Immaculate One" on account of his careful dressing*; "Marie" in that case might refer to the Immaculate Conception. When he started taking less care, he was named Marie Ducas, implying some sort of scandal. [CSW, 2 Oct 1910]
*Wilson defines this as wearing a clean collar at dinnertime. [EAW, 11 July 1910]

26. For most of their time at sea, Atkinson was known as "Jane," for unknown reasons, and occasionally "Helmin", short for helminthologist. He will be known as "Atch" for the rest of the story, so I've jumped straight there, but he didn't get that name until they were approaching Antarctica. No one explains its origin, but it may come from conflating "Atkinson" with "Atchison." It first appears as "Fancy Atch" in Wilson's list of nicknames on 23 Dec 1910.
The original Titus Oates was something of a reprobate in 17th Century England.

27. "Sunny Jim" was a mascot character for a breakfast cereal called Force. Wright claims Simpson's smile earned him the nickname, but I suspect this was an ironic reference to Simpson's lack of humour. Simpson's distinctive profile, on the other hand, resembled Sunny Jim's, and Lillie uses it to maximum effect in a caricature of him dressed in the character's signature red tailcoat and white trousers.
Sunny Jim's profile also inspired the name of a cave in La Jolla, California, the mouth of which has a similar shape. Some forty-odd years after the Expedition, Wright would take a senior position at the Scripps Institute of Oceanography, which is not far from this cave. I wonder if he ever visited.

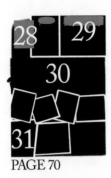

28. WJ 4, ed.

29. "[A]fter dinner we had a general rag, which means turning individuals' clothes inside out for some imaginary offence. This is known as 'furling topgallant sails' and it generally ends in half the mess scrapping together with most of the clothes torn off – and sometimes all." [EAW, 26 Oct 1910]

"We shout and yell at meals just as we like and we have a game which consists of tearing off each others' shirts. I wonder what some of the people at home would think if they saw the whole of the afterguard ... tearing off each other's clothes, the ship rolling, and the whole place a regular pandemonium. [Oates' letter to his mother, 14 Aug 1910, quoted in Diana Preston's *A First Rate Tragedy*, p.125]

PAGE 70

Debenham, who joined the ship in New Zealand, describes a game whose object was to leave no one standing: if you saw the leg of someone standing upright, no matter your position, you gave it a tug to bring them down, regardless of whose team they, or you, were on. [*In the Antarctic*, p.1] Whether this was an evolution of Furl Topgallant Sails or a different game, I don't know – my impression is that the "object" of such "games" was simply a pretext for chaos, and have drawn it accordingly.

30. The most famous depiction of a wardroom "rag" is Dennis Lillie's masterpiece, entitled "A Quiet Sunday Evening on the Terra Nova." This can be found in Griff Taylor's *With Scott: The Silver Lining* or, indeed, on Google.

I had thought the rag was a peculiar invention of Teddy's, but I learned later that a postprandial brawl was a regular thing at Cambridge around this time, and is taken for granted in a *Punch* cartoon about dinner manners from March 1908. Sometimes the past feels only a few layers of paint away; other times it feels like a different planet entirely.

31. "Campbell, Cherry-Garrard and I held the Nursery, which has two doors, against the rest of the Wardroom." [EAW, 11 Aug 1910] This standoff was routed by Nelson and Atkinson going around and attacking the defenders from the other door, which opened from the engine room.

CAPE TOWN

1. Text is from WJ 31, ed. Cherry and Wilson disagree on the date they arrived – Cherry says the 16th, so that's what I've used, but Wilson was the more regular diarist so they probably arrived a day earlier.

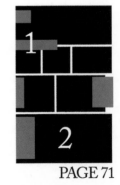

2. The war was the Anglo-Boer War (1899-1902), fought between the British Empire and the descendants of the Dutch who had originally colonised South Africa. It saw the first use of concentration camps (by the British) and the familiar pattern of local guerrillas (the Boers) giving the vastly superior foreign forces a run for their money.

Mr. Bullet Brain lay wounded beside Oates at the standoff where he earned the nickname "No Surrender Oates" (see p.13, or note 8 on p.155). I have conflated him with a wounded Boer who was Oates' neighbour in hospital, in order to show you Oates' broken leg. A Boer

PAGE 71

bullet had shattered his left femur, which subsequently healed an inch shorter than his right. This will come up again later.

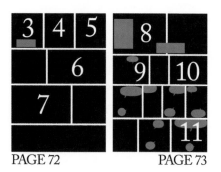

PAGE 72   PAGE 73

3. Teddy describes Oates and Atkinson's holiday amusingly in his expedition narrative. [SWS 36] The one thing Oates wanted to do was go horseback riding, and he spent as much of his holiday as possible doing just that. Oates took Atkinson out on a hunt one day, and wrote home in admiration of his pluck – I don't know if Atch had ever ridden to hounds before. Teddy wonders how two such silent men could find each other such fulfilling company, as conversation would have been next to nonexistent. This may say more about Teddy than about either of his subjects.

4. Having spent all of 23 August writing up, Wilson sent off "a large package" on the 24th, and almost immediately booked a small holiday for himself and Ory. I assume this "large package" was the fabled Grouse Report.

5. Wright took his radiation apparatus to a small town in the interior called Matjiesfontein, to compare readings over land with those he'd been taking at sea. In his memoir he writes glowingly of the well-run state railway through the wilderness, but in a letter home he describes the shoddy workmanship and discomfort of the narrow-gauge track, so this may have been his little joke.

6. For a good time, you can get the full scoop on Birdie and Cherry's adventure with the Williams sisters in Strathie, pp.80-81.

7. Part of the Wilsons' holiday was a ramble over the flowering veldt near Saldanha Bay. "We ... went for a walk up the hills amid a perfect wealth of flowers. ... a sort of enchanted land where the commonest things were all new and beautiful and one's foot crushed new beauties at every step." [EAW, 28 August 1910]

I have committed a crime against ornithology, putting a bird in breeding plumage when it was not its breeding season, but you don't get handed the range of something called a *widowbird* and leave that by the side of the road.

8. The Wilsons actually set sail for Melbourne a week *after* the *Terra Nova* left South Africa, but, being on a steamer, they arrived first. Wilson found the rounds of fundraising dinners, and lobbying the Australian government to make good on its promised grant, to be deeply unpleasant. However, the need to interview some more scientists demanded a longer stay by the Head of Scientific Staff, and with the *Terra Nova* already weeks behind schedule, there was no time to lose.

9. Stoker William Lashly had served with Scott on the Discovery Expedition and his calm, resourceful strength had been a lifesaver when Scott and P.O. Evans fell down a crevasse in Victoria Land. [Scott, *Voyage of the Discovery*, pp.619-620] Lashly will be a life saver on this expedition, too.

10. Simpson had applied to go on the Discovery Expedition, but an iffy medical examination saw another appointed over him. That man subsequently had to drop out, and a lapse of communication kept Simpson from stepping up, so he missed the boat, to his and Scott's regret. In the years since, Simpson had done some studies in Scandinavia and had gone to work at the Indian Weather Bureau in Simla. Scott had had a good impression of him from *Discovery* days, so when the Terra Nova Expedition was announced and Simpson expressed interest in joining, Scott brought him on without even an interview, trusting in his "Indian efficiency" to provide the solid meteorological record which the *Discovery* had lacked. [David Thompson, *Scott's Men*, pp.148-9]

11. If you think extremism and suicide bombers are a uniquely 21st Century phenomenon, you may be interested to learn that in the early 20th Century, the big bad was Anarchism, which employed some of the same tactics. Anarchists were bombing and assassinating around the Western world, and no lesser writers than Joseph Conrad (*The Secret Agent*) and G.K. Chesterton (*The Man Who Was Thursday*) based novels on their exploits.

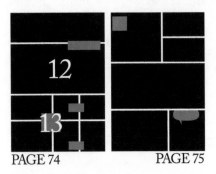

PAGE 74   PAGE 75

12. "The big swell which so often prevails in these latitudes is a most inspiring sight, and must be seen from a comparatively small ship like the Terra Nova for its magnitude to be truly appreciated. As the ship rose on the crest of one great hill of water the next big ridge was nearly a mile away, with a sloping valley between. .... [W]ith a following sea, at one moment it seems impossible that the great mountain which is overtaking the ship will not overwhelm her, at another it appears inevitable that the ship will fall into the space over which she seems to be suspended and crash into the gulf which lies below." [WJ 32-33]

When I was planning out this section, I looked up videos of ships traversing the Indian Ocean, and found a good one of a container ship crossing exactly this sort of swell. The waves were farther apart than I've drawn them here (only two or three would have fit on the page) but it was just as Cherry describes. The video has been gone for a few years now, so if you are crossing the Indian Ocean and get a big regular swell, can you please video it and share it online?

13. [WJ 33] The *Terra Nova* rolled as much as 55° from the vertical. Wright wrote about the "fun" of going aloft in a big swell, in the middle of the night. On the topgallant yards, one would be swung through an arc of 70 feet or more. [CSW, 25 Sept 1910]

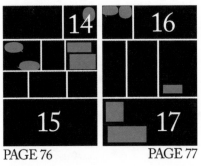

PAGE 76   PAGE 77

14. Weather records for this bit are taken from Bowers' ship journal (not his letters home, which are what is usually referred to as his "journal"). He records a long stretch of fine weather and easterly winds in a quadrant for which the ship's charts mark no easterly winds ever recorded, and hair-raising gales the norm. Scott's instructions to sail north, in the next panel, were in response to an easterly gale [WJ 32], but would also have held true for milder winds such as depicted here. Bad luck with winds will continue to dog the Expedition.

15. "We put him down on the deck, where he strutted about in the proudest way, his feet going flop—flop—flop as he walked ... He treated us with the greatest contempt, which, from such a beautiful creature, we had every appearance of deserving ... They were such beautiful birds that we were loath to kill them, but their value as scientific specimens outweighed the wish to set them free, and we gave them ether so they did not suffer." [WJ 39]

16. "The birds flying around the ship congregate for the main part in the wake, for here they find the scraps thrown overboard on which they feed. I have seen six albatrosses all together trying to eat up an empty treacle tin." [WJ 36]

17. The "Sledging Committee" had representatives from the three main parties of the Expedition – Main (Scott and Evans), Eastern (Campbell) and Ship – with Bowers representing stores and Cherry as secretary.

18. Text on this page is loosely adapted from WJ 39-43.

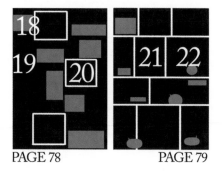

PAGE 78   PAGE 79

19. The *Terra Nova*'s cruet set can be seen at the Canterbury Museum in Christchurch.

20. Bowers had originally been assigned to stay with the ship. In the shore party, he took the place of Rennick, who was not only Bowers' friend but also his cabinmate. Visiting the Antarctic had been a lifelong dream for Birdie, so he was ecstatic to be appointed, but when he found out it was at Rennick's expense, he demanded the change be rescinded. Scott had made up his mind, however – possibly influenced by Rennick having a mild chronic heart problem. [BAE] Rennick was disappointed, but he ended up meeting his future wife while the *Terra Nova* was in New Zealand, so perhaps he wasn't too sad in the end. [Strathie, 82 and Seaver's *Bowers*, 162-3]

21. Cherry describes the squall and the topgallant yard on WJ 40-41. The hailstorm happened the next day; I have compressed them into one episode.

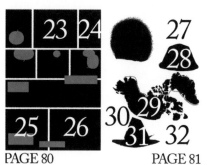

PAGE 80   PAGE 81

22. Silas paints an evocative picture of being aloft in a southerly gale in his journal, being blasted with rain or hail in a 70 mp.h. wind, being unable to see more than a few feet, or hear anything for the flapping of the sails and wind screeching through the rigging. [CSW, 25 Sep 1910]

23. "Below on deck men made hail-balls and pretended they were snow." [WJ 41]

24. Scott "takes no part in the skylarking – but always looks on with a grin." [CSW 2 Oct 1910]

25. Wilson gives an exhaustive description of the fraught time he had with the motor launch, and its several abortive attempts to take Mrs. Scott and Mrs. Evans (plus the mailbag) out to the *Terra Nova*. He closes it with an earnest wish "never … to have more than one wife at a time to look after, at any rate in a motor launch, in a running sea at night time." [EAW 12 Oct 1910]

26. This telegram was sent by Roald Amundsen's brother Leon, who left the *Fram* at Madeira and went back to Norway. By the time the *Terra Nova* arrived in Melbourne, Roald Amundsen had long since left Madeira and was well on his way to the Antarctic. The wording is sometimes quoted as "Beg leave to inform you proceeding Antarctic", which seems to originate with Gran's memoir. As far as I have been able to determine, the original telegram no longer exists, but given Amundsen's terse nature and the fact telegrams charged by length, it's unlikely to have been padded out with so many unnecessary words. Cherry had access to the Expedition's records, and quotes this shorter version, so I see no reason to doubt it. [WJ 41]

27. The text here is mostly taken from WJ 41-42, edited for flow and clarity. I have, however, corrected Cherry's maths: He puts Scott at 43, which was how old he was when he died, not at this point in the story; Amundsen was born in 1872* which makes him four years younger than Scott, who was born in 1868. People at this time often played loose with their age, so Cherry may have been working off received wisdom when he wrote *Worst Journey*, but we know better now.

*Amundsen was, in fact, exactly a week older than Wilson

28. This was nominally a Belgian expedition, but the crew was international, including (among others) not only the Norwegian Amundsen but the American Frederick Cook, who was to make an attempt at the North Pole a decade later. The *Belgica* had to deal with scurvy as well as the psychological effects of the perpetual darkness of polar winter, but Amundsen was unaffected by either.

29. The spot where Amundsen's ship *Gjøa* was frozen in for two years is not far from where Franklin's ships *Erebus* and *Terror,* lost in a previous attempt to find the Northwest Passage, were found in 2014 and 2016. Gjoa Haven is now the launching point for Parks Canada's archaeological work on those ships. Before their arctic misadventure, H.M.S. *Erebus* and *Terror* carried the first expedition to explore the part of Antarctica where our story takes place, and gave their names to the two peaks of Ross Island.

30. Amundsen's dream was to be the first to reach the North Pole, but in 1908 his former shipmate Cook claimed to have done so, followed the next year by fellow American Robert Peary. Both these claims were contested (some now think neither of them really got there) but it took the shine off the prize for Amundsen. There was only one other pole to conquer ...

31. The secret of the *Fram*'s design was a bowl-like sloping hull which would be pushed up by the sea ice as it froze, rather than getting crushed inwards. Nansen had frozen her into the Arctic pack ice and drifted with it for 18 months before he and Hjalmar Johansen sledged to land. Mr. Johansen was now in Amundsen's crew. The *Fram* ran on petrol rather than coal, so could travel light. You can visit her in Oslo, where she has her very own museum!

32. In actual fact, Amundsen waited until arriving in Madeira to announce his secret plans to the crew, giving them the option of catching the next boat home if they wanted. None of them did. Amundsen's book, in which this fact appears, was in Cherry's collection, but I don't know if he read it before writing *Worst Journey*. I have not corrected this statement from the original because this is the impression Scott's men had at the time, and this story is from their point of view.

MELBOURNE

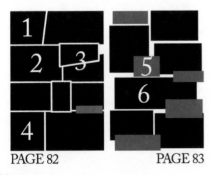

PAGE 82   PAGE 83

1. Little exists in the primary documents regarding Amundsen's telegram – Wilson's diary doesn't mention it at all! – but the editors' narration in Wright's published diaries has enough clues for me to piece together this little episode. [CSW 35]

2. Gran was acquainted with Amundsen, and when Scott visited Norway, Gran made arrangements for the two to meet. Amundsen stood them up. He was, at that point, putting forth the impression he was planning an expedition to the North Pole, while secretly planning to go South. The best way to avoid the awkwardness of the meeting was, apparently, to skip it entirely. [Tryggve Gran, *The Norwegian With Scott*, p.12]

3. Nansen did cable this one word to Scott in Melbourne. The telegram from Keltie actually turned up in Christchurch on 4 November, but it was tidier to include it here. [ACG annotated diaries, 27 Oct 1910, cf. E.T. Wilson]

4. On arriving in Melbourne, Oates acquired 30 tons of compressed fodder for the ponies which they hadn't yet collected, and then he and Atch disappeared. It turned out they went to the Melbourne Cup, which happened to coincide with the *Terra Nova*'s visit. [Davies, p.47] That it corresponds so well with Amundsen essentially challenging Scott to a race, I can only thank a narratively savvy Providence.

5. Narration on this page is from WJ 43, ed.

6. The Admiral on p.84 had previously come aboard the *Terra Nova* for an inspection, and in the crew's quarters found the ship's cat. The men had made him his own miniature hammock, complete with tiny cat pillow and blanket, and he was sound asleep in this when the Admiral came calling. The lofty naval commander was tickled with this sight, but more so when the cat "opened his eyes, looked at the Admiral, yawned in his face, and stretched out one black paw and then turned over and went to sleep again. It was a very funny show and amused the Admiral and his officers as much as anything." [EAW, 17 Oct 1910]

I had limited narrative time available in Melbourne, so in lieu of the Cat Hammock story, I've drawn the bit where a cloud of moths descended on the ship, which was a much more exciting day from the cat's point of view. [WJ 42]

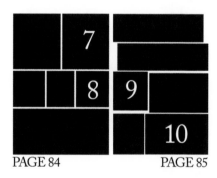

PAGE 84   PAGE 85

7. The naval ships in the harbour were H.M.S. *Powerful, Pyramus, Prometheus*, and *Cumbrian*. [HRB, 15 Oct 1910] They were massive – the *Powerful* was 13,000 tons to the *Terra Nova*'s 700 [EAW, 17 Oct 1910] – which I have played up for dramatic effect. This may not be the literal scale, but as with the warships outside of Cardiff, I wanted to get across what it must have felt like.

8. The Admiral had known Teddy Evans before, and had advised him to leave the Navy "as he would never do any good in it." So, apparently, Evans decided to show off his success by sailing out under full sail, which turned out to be pure hubris as the sail shortly had to be taken in again. [CSW 37] Despite the description of full sail, I have not set the spanker on the mizzenmast here, as it tended to tip the ship over too far and was therefore never used. The spanker booms were removed entirely when the ship was overhauled in Lyttelton. [BAE]

9. Birdie was a great fan of cold water bathing. He and Teddy both seemed perfectly happy to undress, and on this leg of the journey they invoked an old superstition that throwing one's shirt into the sea would bring a following wind. To Birdie's great surprise, the desired wind arose half an hour later, but it came around again by midnight. [HRB 26 Oct 1910]

10. Wilson writes about Cherry sharing his catalogue of specimens on 19 Oct 1910. Cherry did start keeping a sketchbook in Antarctica – he has some adorably naïve sketches of penguin mannerisms, and some quite impressive icebergs. I don't know if he started sketching this early, but it made a nice storytelling point.

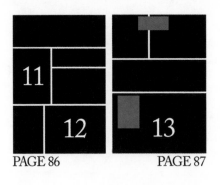

PAGE 86   PAGE 87

11. Simpson, along with several others, went from Melbourne to New Zealand via steamer, so was not present on the *Terra Nova* during this span. Nevertheless, the meteorological record had to be kept up, so someone else is under those oilskins.

12. "Up at 4 a.m. Light enough to see Stewart Island ahead on our starboard bow above a fog bank, and on the port beam a chain of snow-covered mountains with the rosy light of a magnificent sunrise on them and on the snow." [EAW 25 Oct 1910]

13. Antarctic expeditions leaving from Lyttelton all made use of Shed No.5, but despite its fame at the time, no one seems to have made a note of where it was. Some of the photos of the *Terra Nova*'s departure make it look like she took off from the central pier, so I've made that her berth for the duration. Narration is from WJ 44.

NEW ZEALAND

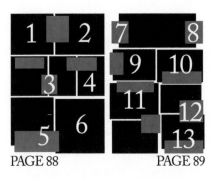

PAGE 88   PAGE 89

1. Birdie had done his apprenticeship on a cargo ship, learning the delicate work of loading and unloading, which has to take into account how the cargo balances as well as organising it spatially. For simplicity's sake, I have drawn him here taking an inventory as items are unloaded, but this task was actually taken over by Scott's wife Kathleen. [Ponting, *The Great White South*, p.7] Not only was this Bowers' area of professional expertise, but Scott had been so impressed with his skills in the weeks prior that he'd promoted Birdie to managing supplies in Antarctica. Birdie was understandably affronted, then, when his job was given to Mrs. Scott, a sculptress with no cargo experience, and wrote some very critical things about her. [Preston, 129] These were not exactly untrue things, but they were negative, and in latter years these comments have been used to cast Birdie as a misogynist. In fact, he held his mother and sisters in high regard and wrote to them as equals, and he sang the praises of Mrs. Evans and Wilson, as well as the spirited, independent, and intelligent young women of New Zealand. His poor opinion of Kathleen is specifically of Kathleen, and one must consider the context in which it was written.

2. Shed No.5, when not in the service of Antarctic exploration, stored grain. Birdie describes great quantities of it, in sacks stacked 30-40 high. [HRB 28 Oct 1910] The *Terra Nova*'s stores occupied only one end of the great space; I've given them more of it for the sake of scale.

3. I have vastly simplified this. Cherry quotes Scott: "We found the false stern split, and in one case a hole bored for a long-stern through-bolt which was much too large for the bolt …" [WJ 45] However, when the *Terra Nova* returned to Lyttelton after dropping everyone off in Antarctica, further investigation found that an erroneously drilled and inadequately filled bolt hole in the bow was responsible for most of the water.

The way they discovered this was quite clever. With the many wooden "skins" on a boat designed for icy waters, where the water is spotted coming through inside might not be where it originally gets in. If water flows in, then it can also flow out, so they drydocked her, built a bulkhead across the forward hold (where the leak had been detected) and filled it with water. Where the water spilled out, there was the hole. The first repair, in the stern, brought pumping down to twenty minutes twice a day; after the second, the ship only needed pumping once every two or three days. Well done, Mr. H.J. Miller & Son of Lyttelton, NZ. [BAE]

4. The aforementioned Mr. H.J. Miller. Thanks to Lizzie Meek of the Antarctic Heritage Trust and Lyttelton Museum, who tracked down a photograph.

5. Northeast Asia plays a significant role in the backstory for this section, so here is a map to set the scene, with modern place names and international boundaries.

Meares definitely went to Nikolaevsk-na-Amure, in Eastern Siberia, in the autumn of 1909. He definitely acquired dogs there, or thereabouts. Where the ponies came from is much fuzzier. The story kept changing – he bought them himself; he sent a friend to buy them in Harbin; he was (according to Anton) cheated by a shifty horse trader. The only written evidence is in a letter from Meares to his father from Nikolaevsk: having spent the winter auditioning dogs for two teams, he hoped to be back in Vladivostok by June, where he would "collect the ponies". [C.H. Meares to Maj. Meares, 18 Mar 1910] Had he bought them when he arrived in Nikolaevsk the previous autumn and sent them down? Had his friend in Harbin sent them there? Had they been bought in Vladivostok, and were being held there for his return? We may never know, however much we would really, really like to. What little evidence exists about the ponies' origins is collected in the very thorough article "They are not the ponies they ought to have been" [Karen May, *Polar Record*, Volume 51, Issue 6, November 2015, pp. 655 - 666], if you want to know more.

Because they were small and stocky, the animals are often called ponies; since that's the word used in the Expedition literature, I call them ponies too. Technically, however, they are Yakut horses. They evolved to thrive in the extreme climate of eastern Siberia, which swings from hot humid summers to winters of Antarctic cold. Dogsleds were used in Siberia when speed was essential, but the Yakut horse was the reliable freight animal of the Russian Far East: they could haul enormous sleighs through deep snow, and lived happily outdoors well below -40°. Like most people, I used to think that the decision to take horses to Antarctica was pretty silly, but the more I learned about the Yakut horse, and saw Meares' photos of them on the job in their natural environment, the more I had to admit they weren't a terrible idea.

That's not to say that Scott's horses were good – the problem was not the idea of horses so much as the particular horses that were selected for the Expedition, many of whom were in poor condition. This will be explored much more in Vol.2.

6. It was pouring with rain when they loaded the animals at Vladivostok, and they had to transfer them from one ship to another at Kobe in blazing hot sun. I have combined the two for this image. From there they crawled down the coast of East Asia, via Hong Kong and Papua New Guinea to Sydney, their fellow passengers increasingly displeased with the livestock sharing their steaming hot vessel. From Sydney they changed ships to Lyttelton, and then quarantined on Quail Island, just outside the harbour, until the final loading and departure.

7. Mr Omelchenko, as the name suggests, was originally Ukrainian; Ukraine had been part of the Russian Empire for hundreds of years, which is why he was regarded, at the time, as Russian. As with geographical place names, I am sticking to nationalities as described in the original records. How Anton ended up on the other side of the continent in Vladivostok I do not know. Why a jockey, who ought to know his horses, would tell a story about being bilked by a rotten horse dealer, is another question. (You can find that story, as recorded by Debenham, in *The Quiet Land*, p.109.) At any rate, he was diligent about taking care of the animals, so we can thank him for that.

8. Dimitri's father had been exiled to Siberia, where he set up the mail delivery business, so Dimitri had been around dog teams most of his life. They ran between Nikolaevsk and the island of Sakhalin, crossing an arm of the Sea of Okhotsk which freezes over in the winter. The modern English transliteration of his name would be Dmitriy Girev, but just as I'm sticking with the historical place names and nationalities, I'm using the spelling which appears in *Worst Journey*.

9. Whoever might have known what, when, about the ponies before they reached New Zealand, Oates wasn't fooled, and had a pretty poor opinion of his charges from the start. "[T]hey are very old for a job of this sort and four of them are unsound," he wrote to a friend. [quoted in Limb & Cordingley, 122] At this point he may have begun to regret declining Scott's invitation to select the horses in Siberia himself.

10. Sometime shortly after the 2010/11 earthquakes in Christchurch, I happened upon an article describing a mantelpiece with Scott's signature on it, which had been saved. The story was that he had signed it while visiting the owner of the house, prior to departure, and the signature later was carved into the wood for posterity. I cannot, now, find any trace of this story. Kinsey's two houses were torn down in 1971 and 2005, so neither of them saw the quakes, but perhaps the signed mantelpiece had moved somewhere else? Or had it not been Kinsey's mantelpiece to begin with? I would love to be reunited with this story, if you know anything about it.

11. WJ 45, ed. The huts had been bought as prefab kits in London, and Davies, the ship's carpenter, was in charge of them. He was not confident in their provider, so erected the huts in New Zealand to make sure all the parts were there, while they still had the chance to make corrections and buy any missing materials. This also gave him the opportunity to train some of the men in how to erect the huts in case the ship had to leave before they were completed. When all the boards were cut to proper lengths they were stencilled and then bundled up again, saving valuable storage space and ensuring easier erection in Antarctica. [Davies, 49] The framework seen here is for the Cape Evans hut; another hut was for the Eastern Party, and a third one, more of a shed, was an outbuilding for the main Cape Evans hut, used for magnetic observations. A fourth hut, intended for a meteorological observatory, was rejected on the grounds of insufficient space in the ship. This was erected instead in the garden of Kinsey's summer house, and would be home to both Oriana Wilson and Dimitri Gerof in turn. Kinsey's house is gone, but this hut has been preserved. It's now known as Scott's Cabin and can be visited on Godley Head near Sumner.

12. Text on this page adapted from WJ 45-46.

13. Aside from cataloguing and marking the stores, Birdie's job also included the reduction of cargo to the bare essentials (nothing more would fit) and cramming as much as possible into the hold. For maximum efficiency, he removed a lot of tinned goods from their cases and crammed them solidly in the lazarette. He even surprised himself with how much he got into the ship. [HRB, ? Nov 1910]

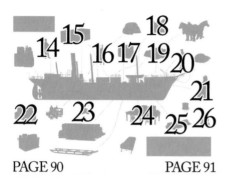

PAGE 90   PAGE 91

14. The 24 officers included Scott's brother-in-law Wilfrid Bruce. He was a captain in the merchant marine, but came as a civilian, to be bossed around by his inferiors in rank and experience. He seems like a really chill and capable guy, who deserved the high opinion everyone had of him, so I regret having to leave him out of the story. Another omission is Francis Drake, who was officially the expedition secretary. As neither Drake nor Bruce landed with the Shore Party, and their presence did not affect the story, I have sacrificed them in the interest of reducing, slightly, the number of characters you need to keep track of.

15. The motor sledges are often mentioned as costing £1000 each, a large outlay for a cash-strapped expedition, but there is no record of the purchase in the Expedition's expenses. There is, however, record that the engineer who was developing them with Scott would retain the patent, so it's likely these prototypes were granted to the Expedition for testing purposes and not sold as merchandise. Certainly everyone refers to them as experimental, and they were treated as such in travel plans. For an in-depth exploration of the motor sledges, see *Scott and Charcot at the Col du Lautaret* by J. Skelton and S. Aubert.

16. New Zealand had developed the industrial freezing and shipping of mutton as far back as the 1880s. The ice house on the deck of the *Terra Nova* was designed to be a great big insulated cooler. "We managed to get 3 tons of ice, 162 carcases of mutton, and three carcases of beef, besides some boxes of sweetbreads and kidneys, into this space." [Scott, 25? Nov 1910]

17. The petrol cases, each containing two drums, were packed in one layer onto the deck of the *Terra Nova* and, in effect, raised the deck by about two feet. This is not the last we will see of the petrol cases.

18. The dogs were chained along the whole waist of the ship, but the ice house was a convenient place to keep them out of the way, and segregate some of the feistier ones.

19. Titus Oates was not impressed with the compressed fodder purchased in Melbourne, so he bought a lot of extra stuff with his own money, and conspired with Bowers to find room for it on the ship. The main hold (A) held 10 tons of it, and 5 tons was stored on deck for easy access on the journey down. The sneakiest stratagem was to fill 3 of the 4 fresh water tanks with pony food as well. Once they reached the pack ice, they would have all the fresh water they could melt. [HRB]

20. When the pony stalls were built, the men's mess was moved one deck down, into their sleeping quarters, which were already crowded. Being under the ponies meant there was a certain amount of leakage after the big storm strained the deck.

> After the gale the main deck under the forecastle space in which the ponies are stabled leaked badly, and the dirt of the stable leaked through on hammocks and bedding. Not a word has been said; the men living in that part have done their best to fend off the nuisance with oilskins and canvas, but without sign of complaint. ... All things considered, their cheerful fortitude is little short of wonderful. [RFS, 7 Dec 1910]

21. "Travelling gear" includes not only skis but tents, Primus stoves, sleeping bags – everything you'd need out in the field.

22. The British Antarctic Expedition 1910 had a number of sponsorship contracts with famous brands of the time – they provided goods for free, in exchange for some sweet sweet product placement in Expedition photographs and some quotable endorsements from famous explorers.

23. "Patent fuel" was coal that had been processed into bricks, which were more efficient to transport and store than loose lumps. Raw coal was crushed and then compressed into blocks with a binding of pitch, bitumen, or some other sticky flammable substance. It was intended for burning in the huts' stoves, but on the sea journey they sometimes had to resort to patent fuel, and it was rather unpleasant to work with – the dust stung one's eyes and the smoke was more caustic than regular coal smoke. [EAW 27 Oct 1910] Because it stacked so neatly, Bowers made a layer of patent fuel on the bottom of the hold which I've marked here as (A), and everything else was loaded on top of that. [HRB]

24. Visiting the Cape Evans hut really brought home to me how many items needed to be anticipated and brought on the journey down. We might all think of tables and chairs and dishes; would you think to bring shelf brackets? Different sorts of nails? Various gauges of piping? Red thread to track the instrument released from a weather balloon? I usually forget at least one thing when leaving the house, never mind taking off to Antarctica for two years.

25. Bolts of spare windproof fabric, both light and heavy weight, as well as some other fabrics, were brought down for repairs and whatnot. That was all the fabric to be had in Antarctica, so it was a closely guarded resource. "The policy of every storekeeper is to have something up his sleeve for a rainy day. For instance, Evans (P.O.), after thoroughly examining the purpose of some individual who is pleading for a piece of canvas, will admit that he may have a small piece somewhere which could be used for it, when, as a matter of fact, he possesses quite a number of rolls of that material." [RFS 11 July 1911]

26. The Expedition's sewing machine was specially constructed by the Singer company to sew every material from silk to thin sheet tin. [BAE]

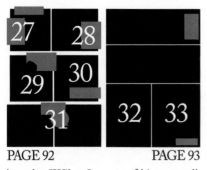

PAGE 92　　　　　PAGE 93

27. In early 1910, while Taylor was studying at Cambridge, he met Douglas Mawson, a fellow Australian and polar explorer, who inspired him to apply for a position with Scott's upcoming expedition. The story of what happened next can be found on p.155 under note 5.

28. Frank Debenham had been interviewed by Wilson when the latter was in Melbourne ahead of the *Terra Nova*'s arrival. "In a brief drive in a hansom cab he asked the applicant a few quite irrelevant questions, and appointed him. In a letter to his wife later, he [Wilson] wrote of his new colleague, 'strong as a horse and has a twinkle in his eye'." [Debenham, *Antarctica*, p.247] This sounds like a slipshod way of screening someone for an expedition, but the most important thing to consider is character and whether the candidate is compatible with the team. Their CV and references can speak to their work, and the medical appraisal will speak for itself, but character you can only ascertain in person. Wilson was very shrewd, as Debenham was by all accounts a wonderful person to have around, and maintained that twinkle for the rest of his life. I would love to know what the questions were!

186

29. Raymond Priestley was a last-minute replacement for Alan Thomson, who had to drop out due to illness. Priestley was still working out his data from Shackleton's Nimrod Expedition of 1907-09 but got permission to leave his specimens and go south again. [WS:TSL 10]

30. Bernard Day had also been on the Nimrod Expedition, in that case having charge of a more conventional motorcar.

31. Herbert Ponting did insist on being called a "camera artist," though his photographs are masterful enough that he probably deserved it. He and Meares had become friends when both were in Japan about five years previously. Ponting had developed his photography skills in California and went on to document Burma, China, and India. His book *In Lotus-Land Japan* had just been published when the Terra Nova Expedition set out, and features prominently in at least one of his Antarctic photos, demonstrating that not only was he adept with the camera but he knew his way around marketing as well.

32. When the *Terra Nova* was in Melbourne, Birdie and Cherry went to see a production of *The Whip*, a spectacle on tour at the time. In the course of the comic, there wasn't time for many diversions in Melbourne, but as Birdie, Cherry, Atch, and Pennell were keen theatre-goers elsewhere in life, they might have gone to see a show or two during their stay in Christchurch. Because Cherry has a panel of his own, I have given his seat to Oates.

33. Wilson was so entranced with the bird life in New Zealand, when he visited the first time on the Discovery Expedition, that he wanted to do a full ornithological survey of the country, which had not yet been done. [Letters to Kinsey, Alexander Turnbull Library] I wonder if he undertook the Grouse Disease Inquiry with the aim of being appointed to that job.

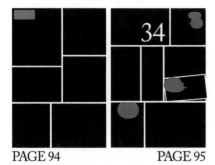

PAGE 94   PAGE 95

34. I have tried to synthesise a few differing sources for Taff Evans' drunk arrival on departure day. [Preston, p.130] Witnesses disagree on whether he fell into the water or was pushed – Bruce (see note 14) implicates Teddy in the latter. Scott had shared some hair-raising experiences with Taff Evans on the Discovery Expedition, and knew what a useful man he was away from the pub, so he was loath to let Taff go, but Teddy's resentment over this incident threatened to break up the Expedition before they even left New Zealand (see note 46).

My depiction of the departure from Lyttelton is mostly drawn from Taylor's book *With Scott: The Silver Lining*. He describes the event in lucid detail, only occasionally diverting to the geological history of Antipodean port cities or a baffling mnemonic for Morse Code.

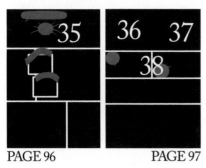

PAGE 96   PAGE 97

35. I don't know which service was read on the *Terra Nova* that day, but a lot of Anglican services end with "The Grace." The centrality of Christianity, specifically the Church of England, to the culture at that time, can be hard to understand from a modern secular perspective. It wasn't that everyone was a believer, but it was a touchstone for all of society, and a foundation for public ritual. Many non-believers went through the motions because that's just *what was done*. Wilson and Bowers were both devout Christians, of very different stripes. Scott was only vaguely theist, but part of his duties as a Naval captain was to lead services, which he did semi-regularly on the ship and in the hut. The remaining expedition members ranged the full spectrum of belief, but everyone enjoyed singing hymns with the pianola. It was something that united people, regardless of whether they believed what they were saying, and for many, the belief wasn't the point so much as the unity.

36. One of the tugs that accompanied the *Terra Nova* out of the harbour was the *Lyttelton*, which you can still visit in Lyttelton harbour today!

37. Rennick was engaged in sending some sort of semaphore messages to someone on land, which "apparently afforded him considerable amusement." [WS:TSL 34] Might Rennick have been exchanging some last messages with the sweetheart he would return to marry? General ignorance of the code prompted Taylor to consider the value of semaphore in the frozen South.

38. WS:TSL 31

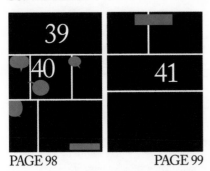

PAGE 98   PAGE 99

39. WS:TSL 34

40. The upper deck of the *Terra Nova* was completely covered with coal sacks and cases of petrol drums, so they overlaid these with bits of scrap wood to make a second, elevated "deck." You can see it in some photos; it does not look like a Health and Safety dreamboat.

41. I have pulled a rather sneaky trick on you. Scott and Wilson were not on the *Terra Nova* between Lyttelton and Dunedin – there were still some loose ends to tie up in Christchurch, so they (and the now sober Taff Evans) took the train down to rejoin the Expedition in Dunedin. Pictured here is the Dunedin railway station, where both the boat train and the Christchurch train would have terminated.

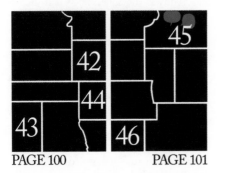

PAGE 100   PAGE 101

42. "I don't think Oates took any interest in social life. He certainly didn't in Cairo when there was much gaiety in the winter. Numbers of people came out from England and there were dances in all the big hotels. But I can't remember Oates going to any of those sorts of things. ... He was a very difficult man to get to know. He kept so much to himself …" [Col. Brooks, quoted in Limb & Cordingley p. 85]

43. Anton demonstrates his famous dancing skills in Ponting's film, which exists in slightly different versions as *90° South* and *The Great White Silence*.

44. "O Tryggve Gran, thou art a man
Who hath compressed within a span
Of three and twenty years, such deeds
That hearing which, each man's heart bleeds
    Among us three;
    And yet though *we*
Are kind to every girl we see,
I have no doubt each lovely creature
Would rather help *you* follow Nietzsche!"

A stanza of the ode T. Griffith Taylor wrote in honour of Gran's 23rd birthday, January 1912. This appears in his official geological report in *Scott's Last Expedition Vol. II* (p.188 if you're looking). I have no idea why he thought it relevant to the physiography of Victoria Land, but I'm glad he did.

45. There was, according to some sources, a mighty row between Mrs. Evans and Mrs. Scott at one of the dances held for the Expedition in New Zealand, of which there were at least three in Lyttelton before the Dunedin dance. Oates reported that "Mrs. Scott and Mrs. Evans have had a magnificent battle ... they tell me it was a draw after 15 rounds. Mrs. Wilson flung herself into the fight after the 10th round and there was more blood and hair flying around the hotel than you would see in a Chicago slaughter house in a month." [quoted in Katherine MacInnes, *Woman With the Iceberg Eyes: Oriana F Wilson*, p.125. The whole topic is explored in some depth pp.124-129.]

This is probably an artful overstatement on Oates' part, but there was certainly some tension amongst Expedition leadership. Bowers suspected the wives of egging on their husbands' egos and inciting competition. [Wheeler, 79] Pennell blamed the female influence, specifically that interfering Kathleen, for getting on everyone's nerves and inflaming tensions on an otherwise happy ship. [Pennell's diary, 26 Oct and 29 Nov 1910] Later in his life, Cherry annotated his Expedition diary, saying that "there was a hell of a row brewing during the dance at Dunedin". In this case, it was not the wives' quarrel, but rather a prospective mutiny by Teddy Evans, who was threatening to resign should Taff Evans be allowed back on the *Terra Nova* after his disgrace in Lyttelton. [ACG notes on 30 Nov 1910; see also Wheeler 79-80]

Was this threat made purely on principle, or was it the product of the female influence, his own ego, and a long string of frustrations? Teddy had originally been planning his own Antarctic expedition, but was encouraged to join forces with the more experienced Scott, whose plans were further advanced and whose fame would attract more public support. In exchange for the funds and personnel Teddy had already lined up, Scott appointed him second-in-command. [Preston, 103-104] It was a prestigious position, but he was an ambitious man and there are times when this subordinate role seems to chafe. Teddy had abundant confidence, a very different leadership style, and his own ideas about how things should be done. Deference was not his strong suit. The dispute over Taff Evans was only one manifestation of this.

On the train back up to Port Chalmers, the morning after the ball, Cherry was in a compartment with Birdie, Titus, and Atch. The latter were inclined to join Teddy in walking out, should he do so, but Cherry refused. He did not record how this disagreement was settled, but the ship left with all parties aboard, so Wilson the peacemaker must have accomplished it somehow. Birdie wrote, "May it never be known how very nearly the *Terra Nova* came to not sailing at the last few hours." [Wheeler, 80]

46. "It was a funny dance as none of our people had dress clothes and all turned up in clean tennis shirts, flannels, or whites, or any other clean garb they happened to have handy." [EAW, 28 Nov 1910]

DEPART DUNEDIN

Few wrote anything between pulling out of Port Chalmers on the afternoon of 29 November, and nightfall on 1 December when the winds were reaching gale force. The most interesting event in those 48 hours was the release of some messenger pigeons, and I have left that bit out. [CSW 30 Nov 1910] The *Terra Nova* was supposed to leave some meteorological instruments with the handful of shepherds on the Campbell Islands on her way south, and give them a quick run-down on how to use them. However, they were making such good time that they expected to reach the Islands in the middle of the night rather than in the morning as planned, so the trip was put off until the return journey. As it happened, the storm was well upon them by the time they would have been approaching, so they couldn't have landed anyway. [RFS and EAW 1 Dec 1910]

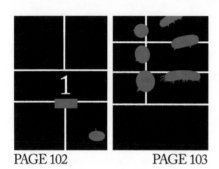

PAGE 102   **PAGE 103**

1. Ponting filmed the departure from Port Chalmers. I have leaned heavily on that for this depiction. The three cheers are in that film; they take on an ironic frisson in light of the tensions we now know existed.

2. "We were boisterously and very cheerily seen off and Ory was with us on board to the last when she had to go off on a tug – and there on the bridge I saw her disappear out of sight waving happily, a goodbye that will be with me till the day I see her again in this world or the next – I think it will be in this world and sometime in 1912." [EAW, 29 Nov 1910] And the tug really was named *Plucky*! [HRB 29 Nov 1910]

3. ACG 30 Nov 1910

4. Departing view of New Zealand once again courtesy of Ponting.

5. According to carpenter Davies, Cheetham could be bribed with beer to delve into his reserve chest of "special chanteys," heavily implied to be the sort of songs unwelcome in a family-friendly graphic novel. [Davies, 41] I will not give him that pleasure here, but he can lead this one.

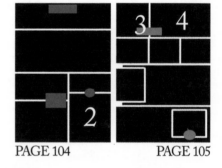

PAGE 104   **PAGE 105**

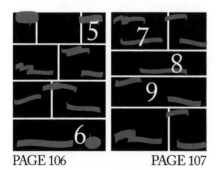

PAGE 106   **PAGE 107**

6. The members who'd joined in New Zealand, including Debenham (here), Taylor, and Priestley, hadn't had the seafaring practice everyone else had had in sailing from Cardiff. This is something to bear in mind when you see what will be thrown at them.

7. "The seas through which we had to pass to reach the pack-ice must be the most stormy in the world. Dante tells us that those who have committed carnal sin are tossed about ceaselessly by the most furious winds in the second circle of Hell. The corresponding hell on earth is found in the southern oceans, which encircle the world without break, tempest-tossed by the gales which follow one another round and round the world from West to East. You will find albatross there—great Wanderers, and Sooties, and Mollymawks—sailing as lightly before these furious winds as ever do Paolo and Francesca. Round the world they go. I doubt whether they land more than once a year, and then they come to the islands of these seas to breed." [WJ 49-50]

8. This device is an Ekman water bottle, used for measuring temperature at different sea depths.

9. WJ 49

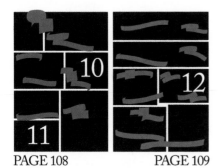

PAGE 108   PAGE 109

10. Sailors believed that cutting one's hair (or nails) in calm weather would bring on fierce winds. [*The Encyclopaedia of Superstitions*, E & M.A. Radford, 1947] Ponting filmed several people getting their hair cut that day, so there should have been no surprise what followed …

11. "We are today at noon in 50°44'S, 170°38'E having made good 191 miles since noon yesterday and the barometer keeps falling, falling constantly and the wind and sea and swell rising all the forenoon and afternoon until it became force 8 on the scale of Conditions of the Sea …" [EAW, 1 Dec 1910]
The scale to which Wilson refers is the Beaufort Scale, a means of quantifying wind speed from Force 0 to 12 based on observed conditions (e.g. wave features or airborne debris), convenient for observers who don't have an anemometer to hand. Force 8, in this case, equates to 39-46 mph or 63-74 km/h. Simpson, the *Terra Nova*'s meteorologist, went on to head the Met Office, the UK's weather bureau, and whilst there he revised and formalised the Beaufort Scale. It's nice to know he had first-hand experience of it.

12. Propulsion helps to steady a ship, so they kept the boilers going as they entered the storm, despite Scott already beginning to fret about the *Terra Nova*'s vast appetite for coal. Just keeping the boiler up to heat burned two tons of coal a day; a great deal more was needed to raise it to a working temperature again if it had been allowed to cool. (When you think of all the steamers crossing the ocean, and the millions of homes and factories burning coal every day, it's not hard to understand why the 20th Century exponentially accelerated global warming.) This panel is just a little reminder that the *Terra Nova* has a steam engine, as well as sail. Not only does it turn the propeller, but it works the mechanical pump that empties the bilges. That is about to become very important …

THE STORM

Three overall notes on the storm sequence:

I.

      I have orchestrated events to have a rise and fall in intensity. Everyone's records of the storm were written afterwards, and their recollections are often (understandably) piecemeal, so it's difficult to figure out exactly what happened in what order beyond basic causality. Even so, I have taken a few liberties with the existing chronology, for dramatic purposes, and clicked separate pieces together to make them flow more efficiently. I hope this still portrays the peril of the storm without being a chaos of anecdote. The important thing is, everything that happens here (except the things marked otherwise) *really did happen*. Just maybe not in exactly this order. And were probably much much worse.

II.

      I have the ship leaning the wrong way. The wind was blowing southwesterly, so she would have been leaning to port, but I have her leaning to starboard, making this a looking-glass version of history. I have done this for one simple reason: This story is about the journey to the South Pole (and back), so for visual narrative clarity, I have tried to keep South on the right, visually. Ideally, no matter where you are in the story, you can look at the direction of travel and know, intuitively, whether they're travelling in the direction of the Pole or away from it. Accurately leaning the *Terra Nova* to port while the ship was facing page right would, in this case, turn the deck away from us and hide what was going on. There are some historical red lines I will not cross, but wind direction is far less important than film grammar, so falsehood it is.

III.

      Usually I cite journals by the date of the entry, but because the journal entries describing the storm are rather long, I have included the page number as well. Wilson's page numbers correspond to the 1972 published journals, and Scott's to the 1913 edition of *Scott's Last Expedition* (Vol.1). Most of the storm narrative in *Worst Journey* is told through Bowers' letter to his mother, so I cite it according to the page numbers in *Worst Journey*.

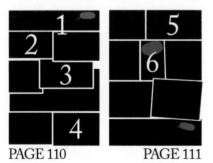

PAGE 110   **PAGE 111**

1. This panel is based on a sketch Campbell did of the *Terra Nova* labouring through high seas, but it's not necessarily this storm. [*The Wicked Mate*, p.48]

2. Being only a short time out from land, the usual suspects were feeling pretty seasick. "I have lively recollections of being aloft for two hours ... and being sick at intervals all the time. For sheer downright misery give me a hurricane, not too warm, the yard of a sailing-ship, a wet sail and a bout of sea-sickness." [WJ 51]

3. "Cases of petrol, forage, &c., began to break loose on the upper deck; the principal trouble was caused by the loose coal-bags, which were bodily lifted by the seas and swung against the lashed cases ... they acted like battering rams." [RFS 2 Dec 1910, p.11]

4. "Bowers and four others went out onto the bowsprit, being buried deep in the enormous seas every time the ship plunged her nose into them with great force. It was an education to see him lead those men out into that roaring inferno." [WJ 51]

5. For some reason – perhaps the stowage of extra fodder – the forecastle stables could only be accessed via the skylight. [BAE] It would be pointlessly difficult to explain this inconvenience to the reader, so I have just used the door. For Scott's lovely description of the ponies at sea, on gentler waters, see WJ 49.

6. "Every case I rescued was put on the weather side of the poop to get a more even keel." [Bowers, WJ 53] They're at the opposite end of the ship here, having just come down from furling the jib. Birdie seems to have been rather possessive of his "carefully stowed petrol cases" [WJ 52].

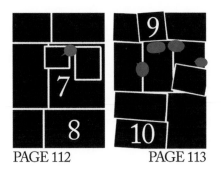

PAGE 112   PAGE 113

7. There were two bilge pumps on the *Terra Nova*: the steam, or "donkey" pump, connected to the engine, and the hand pumps which were worked on deck. The steam pump ran when the engine ran, and once the leak had been fixed, this was usually enough to keep the bilges under control. Now, of course, not only was there the usual seepage of water through the hull, but a lot of water coming in from above. Their old friends the coal balls were up to their tricks again – clumps of coal dust coagulated with oil rolled around in the bilge and would get sucked up by the pumps. "[O]rdinarily, [these] went up the pumps easily;" Bowers wrote, "now however with the great strains, and hundreds of tons on deck, as she continually filled, the water started to come in too fast for the half-clogged pumps to deal with." [Bowers, WJ 52] The solution was to clear the pumps' suction valves manually: "Lashly, for instance, spent hours and hours up to his neck in bilge water beneath the foot plates of the stoke-hold clearing these balls of oily coal dust away from the valves which could be reached no other way." [EAW, 2 Dec 1910, p.66] Lashly was clearing the steam pump: the hand pump's suction was elsewhere …

8. Most of the dogs had been penned over the main hatch, in the shelter made by the two motor sledges in their crates, with the ice house on one end and a wall of fodder bales and coal sacks on the other. This was good to protect them from wind, but it collected water when the ship was wallowing so, to the point where Wilson describes the dogs as "afloat". Birdie says: "We did everything in our power to get them up as high as possible," but "the sea went everywhere." [WJ 53] They tried to get as many dogs as possible onto the ice house, not only for their relative comfort, but because they could be strangled by the collars and chains that kept them from being swept completely off the ship. "Occasionally a heavy sea would bear one of them away, and he was only saved by his chain. Meares with some helpers had constantly to be rescuing these wretched creatures from hanging, and trying to find them better shelter, an almost hopeless task." [RFS 2 Dec 1910, p.14]

9. "Constantly one was caught in the act and a green sea would sweep along the whole deck, rail under, and over one's shoulders … forcing one often to drop everything and cling to the pin rail, or the ropes attached to it, instead of going over the side with tons of water." [EAW, 1 Dec 1910, p.64]

10. The area around the hand pumps had been stacked with bags of coal and fodder, which had to be cleared (i.e. thrown overboard) before the pumping could begin. [WJ 53] "The seas were continually breaking over these people and now and again they would be completely submerged. At such times they had to cling for dear life to some fixture to prevent themselves being washed overboard, and with coal bags and loose cases washing about, there was every risk of such hold being torn away." [RFS, 2 Dec 1910, p.11-12]

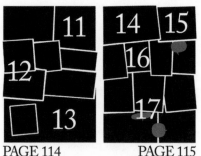

PAGE 114 PAGE 115

11. The ponies' main trouble was the effort of keeping their balance as the ship pitched and listed – the ones on the weather side had an especially hard time as they had to support themselves on their weaker forelegs. "Oates and Atkinson worked among them like Trojans," Bowers recorded. [WJ 53] They were trying to keep the ponies upright, because once a horse fell it was difficult to get him to stand again.

12. "I broke away a plank or two of the lee bulwarks to give the seas some outlet as they were right over the level of the rail ..." [Bowers, WJ 53] The building of a second "deck" of petrol cases had blocked the scuppers (holes in the hull at deck level) through which water would normally have drained. So Birdie had to make some new ones.

13. " ... in the engine-room the water, though not really great in quantity, rushed over the floor plates and frames in such a fashion that gave it a fearful significance." [RFS 2 Dec 1910, p.13] The water in the stokehold was a serious threat. It indicated how much water the *Terra Nova* was taking on, which was concerning in itself. More urgently, though, the boiler was still hot in order to power the engine, which ran the steam pumps and allowed them to steer into the wind for stability. The pumps were clogging, but were still better than nothing. Cold sea water meeting boiling-hot metal was a recipe for disaster.

14. "[O]ver and over the rail, from the forerigging to the main, was covered by a solid sheet of curling water which swept aft and high on the poop. On one occasion I was waist deep when standing on the rail of the poop." [RFS, 2 Dec 1910, p.13]

15. Either side of the bridge was a whaleboat slung on davits, hanging about level with the bottom of the bridge. The one on the lee side "was constantly dipping into the water and was lifted in the davits" until it jammed under the bridge. [EAW, 2 Dec 1910, p.66]

16. "... the pumps were vigorously shaken up,—sickening work as only a dribble came out." [Bowers, WJ 53]

17. "At another time Bowers and Campbell were standing upon the bridge, and the ship rolled sluggishly over until the lee combings of the main hatch were under the sea. They watched anxiously, and slowly she righted herself, but 'she won't do that often,' said Bowers. As a rule if a ship gets that far over she goes down." [WJ 58]

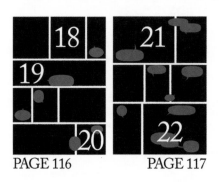

PAGE 116 PAGE 117

18. "You may ask where all the water [in the hold] came from seeing our forward leak had been stopped. Thank God we did not have to cope with that as well. The water came chiefly through the deck where the tremendous strain,—not only of the deck load, but of the smashing seas,—was beyond conception. She was caught at a tremendous disadvantage and we were dependent for our lives on each plank standing its own strain. Had one gone we would all have gone ..." [Bowers, WJ 55]

"Everything everywhere was wet and we were of course battened down – yet all through the night one heard periodically the thud of a sea on the decks overhead and a water cart full of water pour down upon the wardroom floor and table and then subside to a trickle and a drip." [EAW, 1 Dec 1910, p.65]

Bill's cartload of water stands in contrast to the "thirteen Niagaras" Taylor describes flooding the upper bunks in the cabins. [WS:TSL 40] Suffice it to say, a lot of water was coming in.

19. As far as I know, there was no formal meeting to coordinate the emergency responses – Scott only records "we have been thinking of a way to get at the suction of the pump" [RFS 2 Dec 1910, p.14] and Bowers mentions having "all put our heads together" [WJ 54] but this could have happened anywhere, in any company. Everyone had their hands full doing what they could to save the ship, so pulling people away for a meeting would have been unwise, if not impossible. But it was the most succinct way for me to communicate some necessary information and to get everyone on the same page, plus show you the conditions indoors.

In actual fact (or, at least, in Cherry's diary) the bucket chain had started before the furnaces were let out – they took water up and then lowered coal down, the usual means of getting it from the bunkers to the engine room being complicated by the storm somehow. But it is much simpler to explain it all as one unified strategy than a piecemeal series of improvisations. Now you know.

20. I have taken this from Birdie, and given it to Scott. "Had we been able to open a hatch we could have cleared out the main pump well at once, but with those appalling seas literally covering her, it would have meant less than 10 minutes to float, had we uncovered a hatch." [Bowers, WJ 53-54]

21. New faces! Who are these guys? On the left, Williams, chief engineer, and right, carpenter Davies. I have not introduced them by name, as you have enough names and faces to keep track of, but I have tried at least to make them recognisable.

22. Again I have given Scott someone else's words, in this case Bill's: "... when everything began to happen at once it looked as though it had come to save us a great deal of trouble and two years' work, for 24 hours after the storm began it looked to everyone who knew what was going on as though we must go to the bottom." [EAW 1 Dec 1910, p.65] It was Cherry who wondered whether an 800-ton ship had ever been bailed out before, but, as far as I know, only in the privacy of his diary.

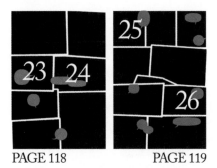

PAGE 118   PAGE 119

23. "The weight of the water in the waist of the ship began early today [2 Dec] to take timbers out of the rail bulwarks, and at 8 a.m. we had one of the bulwark uprights carried away and all the planking so that there is now a big gap in the bulwarks." [EAW, 2 Dec 1910, p.66]

24. Bowers, WJ 54

25. Oates actually brought this report to Captain Scott, rather than Scott visiting him. However, for storytelling purposes, sending Scott forward keeps the focus on him, picks up Bowers, shows us the ponies, and gives us a guided tour of a ship in crisis. Scott tended to jump in wherever there was difficulty, and I wanted to set up that side of his character as early as possible.

26. "... I was soon diving after petrol cases. Captain Scott calmly told me that they 'did not matter'—This was our great project for getting to the Pole—the much advertised motors that 'did not matter'..." [Bowers, WJ 54]

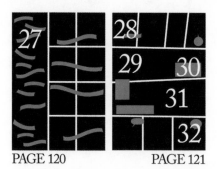

PAGE 120   PAGE 121

27. The officers were divided into two teams which, after the first few hours of this effort, took the bailing in 2-hour shifts, at the end of which "one was so dead-tired that one dropped on to the nearest piece of deck and was asleep in an instant, to be woken up again at what seemed to be the next instant for the next two hour spell." [*In the Antarctic*, p.7] The boiler was still hot, and the water in consequence was steaming, so the lower hold had the atmosphere of a Turkish bath (105°F/40.5°C [Deb, 3 Dec 1910]) while the man at the top was chucking the water into a freezing gale. Those sloshing about in the hot water "found it better at first to do without clothing" [CSW 46], but as mentioned previously, this is a family-friendly graphic novel, so I have imposed a little modesty upon them. Each full bucket weighed about 40 pounds [Deb], though it got lighter as it went up because everyone slopped a little in the passing.

The song here is "Yip-I-Addy-I-Ay," by John H. Flynn and Will D. Cobb, first published 1908 (a 1911 version has slightly different lyrics). They did actually sing this song: "I went to bale with a strenuous prayer in my heart, and 'Yip-i-addy' on my lips," wrote Birdie [WJ 54]. You can find a recording or two online, and the sheet music is on the Library of Congress' website. I'll warn you now, it's a very sticky tune.

28. Cherry dutifully recorded who was on which team of bailers, but I have disregarded this so that you can see Cherry, Birdie, and Bill working together, and also to be able to include Priestley, because I love the fact that Priestley had very bad seasickness and took the end position so as not to be an "inconvenience" to the men below him. [CSW 45] Priestley disappeared at some point and it was assumed the seasickness had finally got the better of him, but it turned out that he had cut his foot on a broken glass. [EAW 5 Dec 1910]

29. Scott and Bowers both name Williams as the one cutting the hole. Davies records that it was him and Lashly. Atkinson only mentions Lashly. I can only assume those three took it in shifts as the bucket brigade did – it was exhausting work – but I've kept Davies at it full time to save confusion. The bulkhead was solid sheet iron and it took 12 hours to chisel a hole large enough for someone to crawl through. If it was anything like the bulkhead still in place on the *Discovery*, this sheet iron was no ceremonial partition but a very solid 1/4-inch-thick wall. Whoever was doing it, it was a cramped and sweltering job in near-darkness over a still-hot boiler, but a job which would ultimately save the ship.

30. Bowers, WJ 54, ed.

31. As implied by Taylor (see note 18), everyone's mattresses were soaked, so they found any out-of-the-way surface on which to catch some sleep. Whatever the circumstances, Pennell was always fastidious about writing up the log.

"Every two hours…" is a line I have made up for continuity, but "Even the fresh water pump" is another extract from p.54. This section is Bowers' letter describing the storm, which takes on a different light when considered in light of the following story from Debenham.

32. Because of the storm, they couldn't get at the fresh water, and with all the hard work they got to be very thirsty. About halfway through bailing out the ship, Debenham saw Birdie serving something from a small keg to the seamen. "The water looked very dirty," he wrote, but in his desperation he didn't mind that, so he begged a pint off Birdie "and felt much better." In his memoir, Debenham describes finding out from Birdie months later that this had been neat rum, but he wrote about it in his journal shortly after the storm abated, so that's how I've drawn it. [*In The Antarctic*, pp.7-8; Deb 3 Dec 1910]

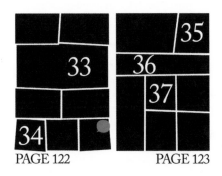

33. "On December 2 the waves were logged, probably by Pennell, who was extremely careful in his measurements, as being 'thirty-five feet high (estimated).'" [WJ 58]

34. This was 10 P.M. on December 2nd [RFS, 3 Dec 1910, 15]

35. Teddy Evans and Birdie Bowers were the ones to go down the pump shaft because they were the smallest. (They also had a love of derring-do, but as far as I know that wasn't part of the decision.)

PAGE 122   PAGE 123

36. When the bulkhead was breached, both Evans and Bowers, and Davies as well, crawled in – Davies to cut into the pump shaft (wood, this time, much faster) and the other two to go down. For the sake of simplicity and clarity I have brought this down to a solo job and left out breaking through the shaft wall, which we can assume Davies did while our attention was elsewhere.

37. According to Teddy [SWS 49], Birdie illuminated his work with an electric torch; Birdie [WJ 55] says they brought down a Davy lamp. I am inclined to believe Birdie here as he was the one holding it, although in my version he's still on the buckets at this point.

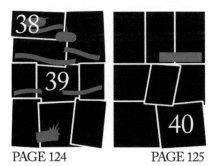

38. The pump was manned by the seamen while the officers and scientists were on the bucket chain. However, I needed Bill on deck to see his rainbow, and our main character has been offstage for most of this sequence, so here they are. Try not to think about how tired this creative decision has made them.

39. "Just about the time when things looked their very worst, the sky was like ink and water was everywhere, everyone was as wet inside their oilskins as the skins were wet without, and things looked very bad indeed in every way, there came out a most

PAGE 124   PAGE 125

perfect and brilliant rainbow for about half a minute or less, and then suddenly and completely went out. If ever there was a moment at which such a message was a comfort it was just then – it seemed to remove every shadow of doubt, not only as to the present issue, but as to the final issue of the whole expedition – and from that moment matters mended and everything came all right." [EAW, 3 Dec 1910, 68]

On the other hand, Debenham went on deck to see what a gale looked like. In retrospect, he thought it must have been about the same time Wilson saw his rainbow, but all he saw was "an abomination of watery desolation". [*In The Antarctic*, p.8]

40. "One [dog] was washed away with such force that his chain broke and he disappeared overboard; the next wave miraculously washed him on board again …" [Scott, quoted in WJ 57-58] Before he could be swept overboard again, one of the sailors grabbed him. [Ponting, 18] "In the morning he was discovered utterly exhausted and only feebly trembling; life was very nearly out of him. He was buried in hay, and lay so for twenty-four hours, refusing food – the wonderful hardihood of his species was again shown by the fact that within another twenty-four hours he was to all appearance as fit as ever." [RFS, 8 Dec 1910] The dog in question was Osman, and he ended up being the most dependable team leader, who will play a starring role in another perilous moment.

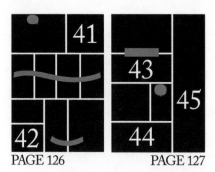

PAGE 126 PAGE 127

41. "I went in again at 4.30 A.M. and had another lap at clearing it." [Bowers, WJ 55]

42. Once the pumps were cleared, a wire cage was put on the end of the pipes to keep out future coal balls. Taylor calls it a "rat trap" – I don't know if it actually was a modified rat trap, or if it merely resembled one, but it meant I got to look up Edwardian rat traps, so no harm done.

43. Campbell and Bowers did undertake an inventory of the upper deck to see what had been lost. Given that everyone's clothes were sopping wet at this point, I have indulged Birdie's love of his dressing gown, "a great comfort as it was not very wet, and it is a lovely warm thing." [WJ 54]

44. Ponting spent the storm "hors de combat on his back with seasickess" [EAW 4 Dec 1910, 69] but he did get up occasionally to bail out his cabin through its sink. [Ponting, 15-16]

45. Once the hand pumps and bailing had brought the water in the engine room down to a safe level, they could relight the fires. After several hours, the boilers were hot enough to power the engine pump, and with this help the bilges were cleared. The engine room would then have been the warmest and driest place on the ship, and Davies records everyone's wet clothes being hung up to take advantage of that. [Davies, 57]

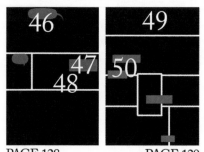

PAGE 128 PAGE 129

46. RFS 3 Dec 1910, 16. The two dead ponies were pulled out via the skylight with the crane.

47. ACG 4 Dec 1910, ed.

48. Many bunks were so sodden that their denizens found somewhere else to sleep. When Gran was on watch, Cherry slept in Gran's bunk; the rest of the time, he found space in the chronometer room, underneath the pantry.

49. Everyone very excitedly rushed for the deck when Gran reported seeing an iceberg on 6 December, but it turned out to have been a whale blowing. [CSW 6 Dec 1910] Reading Expedition journals in the 21st Century, it's surprising how many whales they saw, and how blasé they were about them. The whaling industry had been going hard for a few decades; they had to chase whales into more remote waters, but there was no concern about running out of whales. Seeing them regarded as commonplace really puts into perspective what a huge impact humans had in such a short period of time.

PAGE 130 PAGE 131

50. WJ 59, ed.

51. Cherry's journal at this point is so excited as he relates the best morning he has ever had. There are exclamation points and underlines, and it reads very much as though he is recording it as it happens. He first wrote "we are in the pack" but then crossed out "pack" and wrote "ice". We are about to learn a lot about the pack, so I have taken the liberty of changing it back again. [ACG, 9 Dec 1910]

THE PACK

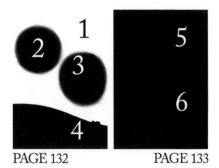

PAGE 132   PAGE 133

1. Text drawn from WJ 59-62, ed.

2. The extent of the seasonal sea ice around Antarctica varies each year, depending on winter conditions. 2014 had a record expanse of sea ice, but in 2019 there was worryingly little. In the latter case, the winter had been warm and windy, so the ice was thin and broke up frequently. Scientists are still not sure why 2014 had so much, but a warm summer may have created more fresh meltwater than usual. Fresh water is lighter than salt, and freezes at 0°C rather than -2°, so an abundance of fresh water on the surface would freeze more readily.

3. There is always a big blob of pack over the Weddell Sea because of how the Antarctic Peninsula interrupts the counter-clockwise circumpolar current. It was into this mass that Shackleton sailed the *Endurance* when embarking upon the Imperial Transantarctic Expedition in 1914, where it then got crushed, stranding the crew. The pack was still there, causing problems, when the Weddell Sea Expedition first tried to find the wreck of the *Endurance* in 2019.

4. Cherry calls this feature an "ice plain" because in 1910 – and indeed 1922, when his book was published – it was not yet proven that the ice was afloat (though it was a theory which Scott supported in 1910). I have changed it to "ice shelf" because we know, now, that it is.

5. Because most of an iceberg is underwater, and pinnacled bergs are all sorts of interesting and unpredictable shapes, there are frequently submarine hazards well away from the visible body of an iceberg, as you can see here with the spur on the other side of the boat. The *Terra Nova* sailed close to one large tabular berg so Ponting could film it, but they were nervous about that and didn't want to do it again.

6. This paragraph is summarised from Scott: "We had been very carefully into all the evidence of former voyages to pick the best meridian to go south on, and I thought and still think that the evidence points to the 178 W. as the best. We entered the pack more or less on this meridian, and have been rewarded by encountering worse conditions than any ship has had before. Worse, in fact, than I imagined would have been possible on any other meridian of those from which we could have chosen." [RFS 10 Dec 1910]

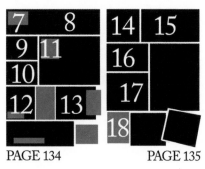

PAGE 134   PAGE 135

7. This line is my invention.

8. The *Terra Nova* men would keep up the football matches through most of the winter at Cape Evans, when light and weather allowed. According to Scott [4 May 1911] Atkinson was "by far" the best player and usually his team won.

9. Meares first took dog teams out for exercise on 15 December, exercising the ones in poorest shape. "They were very short of wind – it is difficult to understand how they can get so fat, as they only get two and a half biscuits a day at the most." [RFS 15 Dec 1910] The biscuits used by the Expedition were not the bite-size morsels we call dog biscuits now, but flattish, squarish cakes a little larger than a saucer.

10. Some of the officers had been practising on ski before this, but skis were issued to everyone in the landing party on 15 December. There is a belief that the British were resistant to ski, but Scott had learned their usefulness on the Discovery Expedition and required everyone to learn how to use them, going so far as hiring onto the cash-strapped Expedition one of the few professional skiers of the time, just to teach them. If there was any resistance to this, it doesn't appear in the journals, where people think skiing a tremendous lark, and go out for ski runs whenever pack conditions allowed any distance of movement. Skiing was even more of an elite pastime in 1910 than it is now, so very few would have had any prior experience with it. By the time they set off on the Depot Journey they were all proficient at least, much credit to Gran.

11. Text on this page is from WJ 72 aside from note 7, the bit about depot-laying, and the last text block, which are my attempts to string things together.

12. Scott's journals are full of grumbling about the pack. "What an exasperating game this is! – one cannot tell what is going to happen in the next half or even quarter of an hour. At one moment everything looks flourishing, the next one begins to doubt if it is possible to get through." [18 Dec 1910] "It is a very, very trying time." [26 Dec 1910]

13. "Any day or hour the floes may open up, leaving a road to further open water to the south, but there is no guarantee that one would not be hung up again and again in this manner as long as these great floes exist. … What to do under these circumstances calls for the most difficult decision. If one lets fires out it means a dead loss of over 2 tons, when the boiler has to be heated again. But this 2 tons would only cover a day under banked fires, so that for anything longer than twenty-four hours it is economy to put the fires out. At each stoppage one is called upon to decide whether it is to be for more or less than twenty-four hours. Last night we got some five or six hours of good going ahead – but it has to be remembered that this costs 2 tons of coal in addition to that expended in doing the distance." [RFS 24 Dec 1910]
   And, of course, they had already lost a good deal of coal in the storm, before even reaching the pack. On 23 December Cherry records that they had under 300 tons of coal in the bunkers, and needed at least 100 tons to get back to New Zealand after dropping everyone off – and they weren't even through the pack yet.

14. While in the pack, Cherry made a catalogue of icebergs in his sketchbook. The sketches here are my copies of his sketches.

15. Blue whales often surfaced close to the ship. "I have been nearly in these blows once or twice and had the moisture in my face with a sickening scent of shrimpy oil." [EAW 26 Dec 1910]

16. An important job in the pack was "watering ship" – collecting ice to melt for the boilers and drinking water. Sea ice is salty, but icebergs are fresh glacial ice. Sea ice that had been elevated by pressure for a sufficiently long time would also be fresh, as the salt drains down to sea level. Having filled three of their four water tanks with horse fodder on the journey down, water had been tightly rationed until they reached the ice, so replenishing was very necessary. Chunks of ice were piled into bunkers either side of the main funnel and melted into the reserves from there. That's the objective of the men in this panel who aren't being silly with penguins.

17. Ponting had this special platform built off the fo'c'sle so that he could film the *Terra Nova*'s bow pushing through the ice.

18. WJ 73

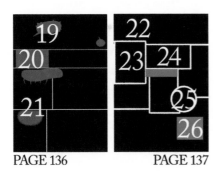

PAGE 136   PAGE 137

19. "[M]ore than once Scott was alarmed by the great shock and collisions which were the result: I have seen him hurry up from his cabin to put a stop to it! But Bowers never hurt the ship, and she gallantly responded to the calls made upon her." [WJ 73]

"Around this time Bowers made a fancy sketch of the *Terra Nova* hitting an enormous piece of ice. The masts are all whipped forward, and from the crow's nest is shot the first officer of the watch, followed by cigarette ends and empty cocoa mugs, and lastly the hay with which the floor was covered. Upon the forecastle stands Farmer Hayseed (Oates) chewing a straw with the greatest composure, and waiting until the hay shall fall at his feet, at which time he will feed it to his ponies." [WJ 75]

Metal-hulled ships had been common since the 1860s, but whalers continued to be made of wood precisely because they had to battle with the ice. A wooden hull is elastic – it can absorb the shock of hitting the ice, and flex under pressure, rather than deforming as metal would. (Think of a wicker basket vs. a metal pail.) Because wood is buoyant, the hull can be dramatically reinforced to withstand both ramming and being frozen in; a comparably strong metal hull would be too heavy. Polar explorers went out of their way to acquire wooden sailing ships long after they had become obsolete, but as more and more wooden ships were retired, their choices grew thinner and shabbier. The *Terra Nova* was old when she was bought by Scott, and was regarded as a step down from the *Discovery*, which had been sold to the Hudson's Bay Company to ply the Canadian Arctic. Shackleton's *Endurance* had been the Norwegian whaler *Polaris* in a previous life, and his other ship on that expedition, the *Aurora*, was well on her way to the knackers' yard. These men were not idiots, nor were they sentimental: wooden ships were simply better for the job than metal ones at the time, even when they were on their last legs.

20. WJ 63 and 64, ed. The Adélies shown on these pages are juveniles, which have white chins for their first year. They hang out in the pack while the black-chinned adults are raising the next generation in the giant rookeries on land.

21. "We used to sing to them, as they to us, and you might often see 'a group of explorers on the poop, singing "She has rings on her fingers and bells on her toes, and she shall have music wherever she goes," and so on at the top of their voices to an admiring group of Adélie penguins.' Meares used to sing to them what he called 'God save,' and declared that it would always send them headlong into the water. He sang flat: perhaps that was why." [WJ 64, quoting EAW 21 Dec 1910.]

22. It was Cherry who fell headlong during ski lessons, but Griff was a more cartoony human, so made a more aesthetic heap of limbs and ski.

23. Lillie's great haul of siliceous sponges occurred much later, but there will be more important stuff going on then, so I moved it here.

24. On WJ 65, Cherry tells of a curious penguin's ingratitude for being rescued from the dogs. The penguins have no natural predators out of the water, and a lot of natural curiosity. In Siberia, sledge dogs were also hunting dogs, and their eagerness to chase and kill any sort of prey would prove to be a problem for more than just the local penguins. Scott describes the pattern of dog/penguin interaction in WJ 86-87: "From the moment of landing [from the sea] their whole attitude expressed devouring curiosity and a pig-headed disregard for their own safety. ... then the final fatal steps forward are taken and they come within reach. There is a spring, a squawk, a horrid red patch on the snow, and the incident is closed."

25. Diatoms are single-celled algae that are incredibly plentiful in Antarctic waters, and give rise to the rich sea life. As with pond scum (another type of algae) in stagnant fresh water, they multiply rapidly when conditions are right, a phenomenon called a "bloom." Around mid-December the seas around Antarctica go from crystal clear to pea soup as the diatoms bloom. They also turn the undersides of ice floes and the white patches on killer whales a greenish-mustardy-yellow colour.

26. Text on this page is from WJ 71.

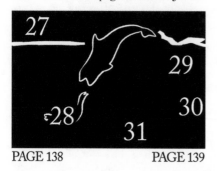

PAGE 138   PAGE 139

27. Originally published in the *South Polar Times* [quoted in WJ 71]

28. This is a leopard seal – or a "sea leopard" as the explorers called it – the hunting seal of Antarctic waters. Leopard seals chase and eat penguins; the more common Weddell eats fish, and the crabeater seal siphons krill through its sieve-like teeth as a whale does with baleen. The Ross seal can also be found in these waters, but the *Terra Nova* didn't encounter any.

29. Silverfish feed both Adélie and Emperor penguins, as well as the Weddell seal.

30. You may have heard of an Antarctic fish with a sugar-like compound in their blood which acts as a natural antifreeze: these are Notothenia, a type of rock cod.

31. Sea spiders (Pycnogonids) live in every ocean, but in the Antarctic they grow to many times the size of their temperate cousins. Dr. Amy Moran has discovered that they breathe with their legs, and their guts drive their circulatory system, but what they eat is still a mystery.

32. I have mashed events from a few different days into Christmas Eve. This panel is referenced from a photo Ponting took on 22 December. The text here is more of my own invention.

33. Wilson often retreated to the crow's nest for a bit of solitude. The *Terra Nova*'s crow's nest appears in a few photos, but the details and interior are based on the *Discovery*'s crow's nest, which you can visit in Dundee.

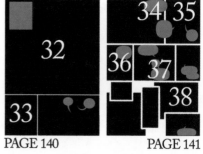

PAGE 140   PAGE 141

34. Atch found an "interesting new tapeworm" in an Adélie on 21 Dec 1910 (EAW) and nothing in the crabeater on 11 Dec 1910 (ACG).

35. Wilson was a committed Christian, who was passionate about science generally and evolution in particular – in fact the natural sciences were, for him, a deep well of spiritual inspiration. This was not the paradox in 1910 that it appears to be today. I want to show, in Wilson, that the conflict between science and religion is a construct of our society, and how the two can happily encourage each other if allowed. The challenge in communicating this is that Wilson, though devout, was very private – Cherry, who among the Expedition members was one of the closest to him, wrote in his foreword to Wilson's 1933 biography of his ignorance of the depth of Wilson's religious feeling, and surprise that he read the Communion service to himself up in the crow's nest every week. [Seaver's *Wilson*, xiv]

36. Cherry was skinning a crabeater seal with Wilson and Atkinson on 10 Dec 1910 when his hand slid down the knife and cut his palm deeply. He lost patience within a few days and started trying to do too much, which kept it from healing. [ACG, various dates Dec. 1910]

37. This is a statement in Cherry's journal for 9 Dec 1910, the day before he cut his hand. However, he is just as enthusiastic about Antarctic life in the following entry, so I'm sure he would have stood by it.

38. "[O]ne has the crow's nest to oneself and one is quite sheltered from the wind when the trap door at the bottom is shut so that one can with comfort read there, while Snowy Petrels and Antarctic Petrels fly a few yards from the edge of the barrel wondering what the creature is inside it." [EAW 16 Dec 1910]

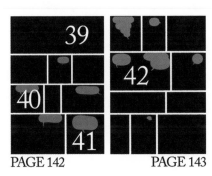

PAGE 142   PAGE 143

39. Hunting for Christmas dinner actually took place on 21 December, which gave the biologists time to dissect the penguins before handing them off to the cook.

40. The Festival of Nine Lessons and Carols is a British institution. It broadcasts live from King's College, Cambridge on the afternoon of Christmas Eve, and while the programme varies, it always starts with "Once in Royal David's City." The tradition only started in 1918, but when it came to picking a carol for a Cambridge graduate to sing on Christmas Eve, there was only one obvious choice.

41. "Wilson went over the floe to capture some penguins and lay flat on the surface. We saw the birds run up to him, then turn within a few feet and rush away again. He says that they came towards him when he was singing, and ran away again when he stopped." [RFS, 21 Dec 1910]

42. What they are doing here is pithing the penguins – one sticks a small sharp rod into the skull via the base of the neck and, essentially, scrambles the brain. It is a fast and humane way of killing a penguin, which is a most resilient creature otherwise.

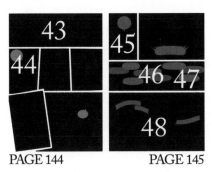

PAGE 144   PAGE 145

43. Cherry really was chased by the dogs, albeit on a slightly earlier penguin-hunting expedition. [WS:TSL, 69-70] I've trimmed down Taylor's version to fit into one page.

44. The dogs were Russian, so were trained to Russian commands – not human words, but a local vocabulary for dog driving. Meares had spent some years in Russia and was fluent in both human and canine Russian. The dogs' commands were "ki" (right), "tchui" (left), "itah" (right ahead), and "paw" (stop). [RFS 12 Jan 1911]

45. They did toast "To absent friends" [WJ 76]: it's the traditional Royal Navy toast for Sunday, and Christmas 1910 was indeed on a Sunday. I give you this fact here so that I can disappoint you in future by holding the Rule of Three higher than Naval tradition.

46. Ponting describes penguin tasting like jugged hare in *The Great White South*, p.43.

47. The men did have some of that frozen New Zealand mutton for their feast, which they ate at midday. "[T]here was plenty of penguin for them, but curiously enough they did not think it good enough for a Christmas dinner." [WJ 76]

48. "For five hours the company has been sitting round the table singing lustily; we haven't much talent, but everyone has contributed more or less, 'and the choruses are deafening. It is rather a surprising circumstance that such an unmusical party should be so keen on singing. On Xmas night it was kept up till 1 A.M.'" [RFS, 25 Dec 1911] (Some of this is from a letter, grafted into the published journal.)

They didn't only sing Christmas carols – Meares wrote a song which ran through most of the characters of the Wardroom, and Titus Oates won applause for something called "The Vly on the Turmuts." So it's no surprise that a lot of penguins were around "to satisfy their curiosity."' [CSW, 26 Dec 1910]

At some point on Christmas, Bernard Day shared with Cherry his design for "A Fly-Trap of Marston" –

The fly climbs the ladder at left, walks along the plank, sees the electric light and the piece of cheese and thinks, "Aha, this is a trap!" so keeps walking. He climbs down the ladder on the right but oh no! The bottom rungs are missing, and he falls onto the block of marble and breaks his neck. [ACG 25 Dec 1910]

This had me in stitches when I found it in the archive. Maybe it needs a full morning of transcription as a warm-up.

Cherry recalls this as being the most Christmassy Christmas he had ever had; Scott, on the other hand, looking at the solid pack in every direction but behind, the thick grey sky, and intermittent snow, grumpily called it "altogether too Christmassy".

ANTARCTICA

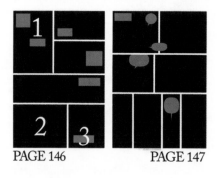

PAGE 146   PAGE 147

1. Text loosely edited from WJ 77-78

2. I have left out a whole other storm here. The barometer dipped nearly as low as anyone had seen before, and those prone to seasickness found that their tolerance had worn off during the long calm spell in the pack. Luckily, though they were out of the main pack, they found a stream of ice to shelter behind and escaped the worst of it, but they had to burn more precious coal to keep the ship in position.

3. This line, and the following page, are from WJ 80, almost exactly transcribed from ACG 1 Jan 1911.

PAGE 148

4. I decided on this as the final image of Vol.1 when reading Cherry's diary – the way he described it, it was the perfect closing image, and I was surprised he hadn't used it the same way I intended to. (It's buried a few pages into the following chapter of the book.)

Nearly a year later, after I'd written the script, I was back in the archives looking through his sketchbook for a promised map of their landing site at South Trinidad, when I found the most evocative pencil sketch of the view he'd outlined so clearly in words. This page is based as closely on that sketch as I could manage. It really felt like he'd left it just for me, to make sure I got it right.

I have given the impression that the great unveiling occurred just before midnight, but it was in fact 10:30 PM; Cherry went to bed again and was woken by the "rowdy mob" ringing in the New Year through the Nursery. "I expected to be hauled out, but got off with a dig in the ribs from Birdie Bowers." [WJ 80-81]

THANK YOU FOR READING!

FURTHER READING

If you've enjoyed this, and want to know more, the obvious place to look is the original *Worst Journey in the World*. Cherry's magnum opus is profound, immersive, and moving, and quite rightly tops lists of great travel literature. It's also nearly 600 pages long. If the length doesn't scare you off, the dry introductory chapter about the history of polar exploration might do. You have my permission to skip this if you wish. I know why Cherry included it, but the story is perfectly comprehensible without it, and would be a shame to miss.

If you'd prefer a lighter start, the book I usually recommend to people embarking on their Terra Nova journey is *A First Rate Tragedy* by Diana Preston. It's an easy and entertaining read, and moves briskly through the history, but there's still room for the delightful anecdotes that bring the story and people to life. Nevertheless it's also thoroughly researched and cited, and provides a grounding in Scott's biography and first expedition, both of which informed decisions made on the last. Very much "the good parts version."

In the 1970s and 80s it became fashionable to bash Scott and his Expedition, sometimes straining the historical record to do so, and colouring a generation's perception of the story. Subsequently, descendants and academics published a great number of Expedition diaries that had hitherto been locked up in archives or private collections, and these have helped set the record straight. Now all of us can share the joy of primary documents! My favourite diary is probably Debenham's (published as *The Quiet Land*), but Wright's (published as *Silas: The Antarctic Diaries of Charles S. Wright*) has some laugh-out-loud moments sprinkled in amongst the science. Scott, Wilson, Campbell, Bowers, Gran, and Lashly have also had their diaries published in some form or other; Lt. Evans, Ponting, Taylor, Priestley, and Davies wrote their own accounts of the Expedition after they got back. (See the Bibliography for details.)

For a more comprehensive portrait of Cherry, you must seek out Sara Wheeler's biography *Cherry: A Life of Apsley Cherry-Garrard*. The three years of the expedition may have dominated his own memory, but his life involved a lot more than that, and Wheeler tells it admirably.

If a picture is worth a thousand words, then whole libraries are contained in *With Scott to the Pole: The Terra Nova Expedition 1910-1913: The Photographs of Herbert Ponting*, probably the single most complete book of Expedition photos. Actual moving pictures of Expedition people, alive and well, exist as *The Great White Silence* (Ponting's original silent film, recently restored by the BFI) and *90° South* (the 1933 "talkie" edit, wherein both Ponting and Teddy Evans introduce the film on camera). Complement these with *The Lost Photographs of Captain Scott*, compiled by David M. Wilson – Scott was a rookie photographer but had real talent, and provides a valuable alternative point of view.

There are many, many more books than these – but that should give you a start!

ACKNOWLEDGEMENTS

A creative work may have one parent, but could not be brought into the world without many midwives and nurses. Over this book's long gestation, a great number of people and organisations have offered a great deal of help and encouragement. Without them it would be a much poorer thing, if it existed at all. In roughly chronological order, I would like to thank:

Kate McAll, Stef Penney, and the BBC Radio Drama Department, whose talent and hard work changed the direction of my life, for which I will be forever grateful.

Karen May, the first to believe in this book and abettor of Scott nerdery, who introduced me to academia and the Joy of Primary Documents, and set the highest example of diligent research.

Sydney Padua, whose footsteps in the snow from animation to copiously annotated historical graphic novels I had only to follow, and whose warnings I blithely ignored.

Tony Cliff, who changed my mind about comics, introduced me to Radio 4, and has been an eternal spring of artistic education and enlightenment, not to mention friendship.

Glen Keane, who took a chance on damaged goods, got me to love drawing again, and had the generosity of spirit to set me free. This book is in colour because of him.

The Scott Polar Research Institute, keeper of the Precious Things, enabler of Special Interests. Most particularly Charlotte Connelly for ready help with both polar history and history of science, as well as being ambassador for this project; Naomi Boneham and Laura Ibbett for satisfying my hunger for goodies from the archive; and Naomi Chapman for everything else.

Hugh Turner, who has been equally open with his library and his friendship.

Francis Spufford, who started out offering expert feedback, and ended up contributing more material help to the production of this book than I could ever have dreamt of asking.

Paul Beattie, who bought me precious time while my Patreon got up to speed.

J.B. Williams, for polar fellowship, a keen eye, and Francis Davies.

The San Diego Maritime Museum, whose *Star of India* is the closest I will ever get to setting foot on the *Terra Nova*, allowing me to walk the ship in my head and on the page.

Discovery Point and the Dundee Heritage Trust – everything I've drawn below decks is thanks to my days loitering with ghosts on the R.R.S. *Discovery*. Long may she grace the Tay.

The Jubilee Sailing Trust, for a tremendous week on the SV *Tenacious*. Whatever I've got right about tall ship sailing is thanks to them; whatever I've got wrong is my own fault.

Dr David M. Wilson and The Wilson Museum, Cheltenham, for perpetuating the influence of the most wonderful person who ever lived. He is wanted more now than ever.

Anne Strathie, for fact-checking, quote-hunting, and sharing confidences.

The Antarctic Heritage Trust, for going above and beyond to preserve the Heroic Age legacy and communicate it into the future. For this volume especially, special thanks to Lizzie Meek, not only conservator extraordinaire but proprietress of Lyttelton esoterica.

The Canterbury Museum, Christchurch, for their Antarctic History collection, and responding to seismic challenges with astonishing generosity in digitised documents.

The Alexander Turnbull Library, for allowing me to make off with as many screencaps of the Kinsey archive as I could cram onto my flash drive in two days. Such wealth, so freely given.

The National Science Foundation, for deigning to elevate me to the ranks of Antarctic Artists & Writers. Most enthusiastic thanks to Elaine Hood, whose competence and good cheer never faltered, when lesser humans' would have done.

Caitlin Like and Rhianna Wynter, without whose flatting skills and diligence I might *still* be working on these pages …

And to anyone who should be on this list and isn't – a lapse of memory, not of gratitude.

PATRONS

To make a book is one thing; to eat while doing so is another. These excellent souls kept a roof over my head and food in my pantry while I turned time and calories into words and drawings:

Abbe Wiesenthal, Abby C, Alisdair Cain, adam, Adam S, Adrian Hashimi, Adriana Eidel, Agnes Salek, Alan Caum, Alex Caligiuri, Alex Ramirez, Alex Sylvester, Alexander Campbell, Alexandra Bowman, Alexandra Isern, Alice Broadribb, Alice Fletcher, Alison, Allie, Amanda Aiken, Amy Silva, Andrea M. Burfeid Castellanos, Andrew Airriess, Andrew Humphreys, Ann Boyles, Anna Parker, Anne Benning, Anne Strathie, Ariana Scott-Zechlin, Arianna von Habsburg, Bad Juju, Barbara Laub, Barbara Schuler, Becca Hovey, befroy, Ben Hatke, Ben Quinn, Bethany Wells, BiancaIcaras, Bre Galloway, Brenda Halpain, Brian McDonald, Bridget Young Linehan, brinsonmarie, Bryan Kiechle, c, Caitlin Greenwood, Camille Hunt, Cara, Carey Fluker Hunt, Carlos Luz, Carolyn Paplham, Cassandra Jarvie, Catherine Nieva, Cathy Durot, Cato, CC Shermer, Charlotte Connelly, Chaweinta Hale, Chelsea & Emily Davis, Cheyenne Smith, Chris Sheridan, Christine, Cole, Colin Stanton, Cora Schim van der Loeff, Cozy Robot, Crys Kirk, Cyd, Dafna Pleban, Damian Marley, Dan A, Dan Long, Daniel King, David Gian-Cursio, David Gray, Deborah Wood, Dennis Glover, Deven Greves, Diana Davis, Diana Payton, Dianna Gabbard, Dom, Don Perro, Donal Chan, Donna Gaffney, Dustin Rimmey, Elaine Sue Hood, Elena Felici, Elisa Balestri, Elisabeth Alster Hardy, Elizabeth Bruton, Eloise Sherrid, emeraldgreaves, Emile, Emilee Waugh, Emily Gilbert, Emily Mackey, Emily Rigby, Emma Dinkelspiel, Emma Heyn, Emmett Santo, Eppo Steenhuisen, Eric McCloy, Erin Fields, Erkshnrt, Euphonious Nelson, Evak, Eve Mary Oakley, F A Plunkett, Faye Simms, fireflysummers, Fnord, fran knapp, Francesca Buchko, Francis Spufford, Freddie Lee, Freya Hotson, Gabriel Liston, Gabriel Whitney, GARBeard, Gary Murphy, Gee, Gerri Airriess, Anonymous, Giselle Airriess, GlassCreatedByJessi, Glen Keane, Greg S. Reese, Guy Bolton King, Guy Cavet, H0lyhandgrenade, Hannah Haverkamp, Hannah Hoersting, Hannah Lowell, Hans, Hans Ranke, Hazel Kasusky, Heather Moritz, Hedvig Widmalm, Helen Greetham, Henry Barnosky, Henry Treadwell, Holly Manning, Huma Jehan, Iain M Barker, Idle Doodler, InkFire, Isabel Suhr, Isabel Wilson, Ivan Syniepalov, J Davis, J.B. Williams, Jack Belloli, Jackson Vanfleet-Brown, Jacques-André Blouin, James C. Sullivan, Jean Kang, Jennifer Eggleston, Jennifer Porter, Jenny Harris, Jessica Mahon, Jim Bending, JJ Gauthier, jo meyer, Joanna Quinn, Johanne D, John Finnemore, John Inverso, John Sauverin, John Wilson, johnny dangerously, Joi, jon doc, Joseph Pearl, Josephine Siedlecka, Julia Gottschalk, Julie Botten, Julie Parsonnet, Karen May, Karen White, Karin L. Kross, Kat, Kat Mawhinney-Kam, Kate, Katherine Taylor, Kathryn Miller, Katie, Katie Weishoff, Katrina van Grouw, Kel McDonald, Kell, Kelly, Kelly Landes, Kenneth Kufluk, Keres, Kevin Gambrel, Kirsten Carlson, Kit Lane, Kkris, KTH, Lana Dragičević, Laura, Laura Fissel, Laura J Testa-Reyes, Laura Morley, Laura Omdahl, Laura Truxillo, Lena Strid, Leonard Richardson, Lesley Urasky, Linda Hiemstra, Lindsay Wells, Lindsey Kitchener, Lissa Treiman, LJ, Lloyd Tunbridge, Lucie, luckyjean, Lucy Bellwood, Lucy Carty, Lucy Stevens, Lydia Johnson, Lynn Maudlin, Maggie L, Maor Schreiber, Margaux De Pauw, Margie & Eric Daniels, Mark Hulkovich, Marmagenta, Marta Karbowiak, Mary, Mary Bull, Mary Jo H Croake, Matt Aytch Taylor, Matthew Jeppesen, McKenzie Marcs, Megan Lerseth, Meghan Hawkes, Megs Peters, Melissa Lattimore, Merja Polvinen, mica (the mineral), Michelle McKinney, Mike keating, Mike Sharples, milky, Miriam R Grønli, mkreed, mo, Molly Murakami, Monica Marion, NAN YIN, Nancy Kindraka, Naomi Hemmings, Natalie Asplund, Natalia Chwialkowski, Neha Dinesh, Niamh, nicholas collins, Nicholas Massa, Nicole Arruda, Nikolas Lamarre, Noé Ramalleira Fernández, Nonstop Pop!, Nora Kunkeler, Norman Webb, Oliver Richards, Olivia Shan, Panayiota Blassis, Patricia Worsnip, Paul Beattie, Paul Bussey, Paul Cherry, Pauline, Павел Миронов, Pete Arundel, philomena hughes, Pilfering Apples, Poline Cedric, R. Wesley Nipper, Rüsselbiene, Rachel Avila, Rachel Barenblat, Rachel Smith, Raquel Torna, Raymond, RB Bartgis, Rebecca Breu, Rebecca E. Williams, Rebecca Gautrey, Rebecca Gleeson, Rebecca McVeigh, Rebecca Sodari, Rebekah Walker, Renny Richardson, Richard Knights, Rob Ferguson, Rob Lavoie, Robert Snowden, Rose Driver, Rose Sawyer, Roseanne de Beaudrap, Ross Blocher, Roxanne, Rufus Hart, Rwynter, Sabrina Cotugno, Sally Cassels, Sally Wongso, Samantha Davies, Samantha Kramer, samma, sandwichgirl, Sanne, Sara Ridge, Sarah, Sarah Barnard, Sarah Johnson, Sarah Parker-Shemilt, Sarah Pickman, Sasha Schotzko-Harris, Scott Greenlay, Sean Covernton, Seiko, Shane K. Sowell, Sharyle Doherty, Shaun, Shaun O'Boyle, silriven, simon stern, Sir_Yb_Mits, Sonya Nygard, Sophie Iles, Sophie Philips-Roberts, Squirrels for short, Stacy B, Stephanie Nickols, Stephen Crowe, Stephen Sepaniak, Stephny Campbell, Steve Muench, Steven Healer, Strampunch, Sue Dowling, Susan Nachtigal, Susan Rose, Sydney Padua, Sylvia Morris, T.E. Masuda, Taylor, Taylor Sterry, Tessa, Thisfox, Thomas Mclean, Tiffany Mercer, tk, Toasty, Tony Cliff, Tuy Tran, Валерия Самсонова, Vanessa Salas Castillo, vegemiteknees, Vera Tenei, Viola Toniolo, William Bradford, William Tate, Woodspurge, Zachary Guiliano, Zephronias, Zippy Wafflebuns, Zoe R. Courville, and Zoe Stock — *Join them for Vol.2 at patreon.com/tealin*

BIBLIOGRAPHY

Aubert, Serge, Judy Skelton, Yves Frenot, and Alain Bignon. *Scott and Charcot at the col du Lautaret*. Grenoble: Lautaret Alpine Botanical Garden, 2014.

Cherry-Garrard, Apsley. *The Worst Journey in the World*. London: Chatto & Windus, 1951.

Davies, Francis. *With Scott Before The Mast*. ed. Joy Watts. Cheltenham: Reardon Publishing, 2020.

Debenham, Frank. *Antarctica*. New York: The Macmillan Company, 1961.

Debenham, Frank. *In the Antarctic*. Banham: The Erskine Press, 1998.

Debenham, Frank. *The Quiet Land: The Antarctic Diaries of Frank Debenham*. ed. June Debenham Back. Huntingdon: Bluntisham Books, 1992.

Evans, Edward R.G.R. *South With Scott*. London and Glasgow: Collins Clear-Type Press, 1945?

Flynn, John H, and Will D Cobb. *Yip I addy I ay!* Will D. Cobb, New York, 1908. Notated Music. https://www.loc.gov/item/ihas.100006072/.

Gran, Tryggve. *The Norwegian With Scott*. trans. Ellen Johanne McGhie, ed. Geoffrey Hattersley-Smith. Her Majesty's Stationery Office, 1984.

Huxley, Leonard, ed. *Scott's Last Expedition*, Vol. II. London: Smith, Elder & Co., 1913.

Lane, Allen. *Scott's Men*. London: Penguin Books Ltd, 1977.

Limb, Sue and Patrick Cordingley. *Captain Oates: Soldier and Explorer*. Barnsley: Pen & Sword Books Ltd, 2009.

MacInnes, Katherine. *Woman With The Iceberg Eyes: Oriana F. Wilson*. Cheltenham: The History Press, 2019.

May, Karen and George Lewis. "'They are not the ponies they ought to have been': Revisiting Cecil Meares' purchase of Siberian ponies for Captain Scott's British Antarctic (Terra Nova) Expedition (1910-1913)" *Polar Record* 51, issue 6 (November 2015) 655-666

Ponting, Herbert G. *The Great White South*. London: Duckworth, 1932.

Ponting, Herbert G., Henry R. Bowers, H.J.P. Arnold, Beau Riffenburgh, Liz Cruwys, Julian Dowdeswell, Ranulph Fiennes. *With Scott to the Pole*. London: Bloomsbury, 2004.

Preston, Diana. *A First Rate Tragedy*. London: Constable & Co., 1997.

Scott, Robert F. *Scott's Last Expedition*, Vol. I. ed. Leonard Huxley. London: Smith, Elder & Co., 1914.

Scott, Robert F. *The Voyage of the 'Discovery'*. London: John Murray, 1943.

Seaver, George. *'Birdie' Bowers of the Antarctic*. London: John Murray, 1951.

Seaver, George. *Edward Wilson of the Antarctic*. London: John Murray, 1938.

Spufford, Francis. *I May Be Some Time: Ice and the English Imagination*. London: Faber and Faber, 1996.

Strathie, Anne. *Birdie Bowers: Captain Scott's Marvel*. Stroud: The History Press, 2012.

Taylor, T. Griffith. *With Scott: The Silver Lining*. Norwich: Bluntisham Books and Erskine Press, 1997.

Wheeler, Sara. *Cherry: A Life of Apsley Cherry-Garrard*. New York: Random House, 2002.

Wilson, David M. and D.B. Elder. *Cheltenham in Antarctica*. Cheltenham: Reardon Publishing, 2000.

Wilson, David M. *The Lost Photographs of Captain Scott*. London: Little, Brown, 2011.

Wilson, David M. and C.J. Wilson. *Edward Wilson's Antarctic Notebooks*. Cheltenham: Reardon Publishing, 2011.

Wilson, Edward A. *Diary of the 'Terra Nova' Expedition to the Antarctic 1910-1912*. ed. H.G.R. King. London: Blandford Press, 1972.

Wilson, Edward A. *Diary of the Discovery Expedition to the Antarctic Regions 1901-1904*. ed. Ann Savours. London: Blandford Press, 1966.

Wright, Sir Charles S. *Silas: The Antarctic Diaries and Memoir of Charles S. Wright*. ed. Colin Bull and Pat F. Wright. Columbus: Ohio State University Press, 1993.

Unpublished Sources:

Thomas H. Manning Polar Archive at the Scott Polar Research Institute, Cambridge, UK
  A. Cherry-Garrard archive
  E.L. Atkinson archive
  H.L.L. Pennell archive
  G. Seaver archive
  O.F. Wilson archive
  British Antarctic Expedition 1910-1913, Miscellaneous Papers

British Columbia Archives at the Royal British Columbia Museum, Victoria, B.C., Canada
  C.H. Meares fonds
  C.S. Wright fonds

Sir Joseph Kinsey archive, Alexander Turnbull Library, Wellington, NZ

A. Cherry-Garrard personal library and ephemera, private collection, UK

H.L.L. Pennell journal, Canterbury Museum, Christchurch, NZ

worstjourney.com